CHRONICA BOTANICA

AN INTERNATIONAL BIOLOGICAL AND AGRICULTURAL SERIES

Consulting Editor, Frans Verdoorn

No. 18

A GUIDE TO THE

HISTORY of BACTERIOLOGY

THOMAS H. GRAINGER, JR.

ASSOCIATE PROFESSOR OF BACTERIOLOGY

LEHIGH UNIVERSITY

THE RONALD PRESS COMPANY · NEW YORK

Library of Congress Catalog Card Number: 58–13749
Printed in the United States of America

PREFACE

This guide, with selected list of reference sources, has been compiled for use in the course "History of Microbiology" offered at Lehigh University. The course is designed to stimulate interest in and an appreciation for the history of this science and, in addition, to present a survey of representative bibliographical tools for contemporary interests. Thus, this small book may serve a cross-section of readers—research workers, librarians, bibliographers, and students of the history of bacteriology and science.

The short introduction explains the purpose and meaning of why one should study the history of any science. This is followed by the selective annotated* bibliography, which is divided into four parts: the first section is a guide to the literature of bacteriology; the second section is concerned with the history of bacteriology, with special reference to specific areas; and the third and fourth sections contain biographical references in bacteriology. Thus, this bibliography is an attempt to bring together in convenient form references to the most important contributions to the literature of bacteriology and to the development of its history.

Under each subject the important works are arranged in alphabetical order and are, for the most part, self-contained units which can be utilized without too much reference elsewhere. Several of the sections will include duplication of items; this is necessary since several publications serve more than one function. No attempt has been made to provide a complete list. It is *selective*; it omits many minor items and attempts to omit as many duplicated entries as possible. The needs of English-reading students were obviously given priority. Every effort has

*McClelland, E. H. 1943. Abstracts and annotations. Spec. Lib., **34**, 363–372. Annotation—"Purpose...is only to characterize the article, merely as an aid to the reader in deciding whether or not he should see the original."

been made to check the accuracy of the references and other data, but this has not been possible in every case.*

The bibliography is based primarily upon the author's own library and the excellent facilities of the library of Lehigh University. Several important publications may easily have escaped my attention. Every bibliography contains errors of omission. It is hoped, however, that these have been kept at a minimum. Thus, the author is bound to have overlooked some items or to have included items that others, perhaps, would omit. Corrections and suggestions will be gratefully received.

Within this modest scope, it is hoped that it will in some measure fulfill its objective of assisting those who are interested in the record of past achievements in bacteriology and in the further development of this branch of science. At best, this may be considered worthy to serve as a starting point for something better.

I am greatly indebted to the great historian of science, Dr. George Sarton, for his stimulation concerning this brief work. Thanks are extended to Dr. Frans Verdoorn for his numerous suggestions.

Thomas H. Grainger, Jr.

Bethlehem, Pennsylvania
July, 1958

*An entry marked with an asterisk means that the publication has not been seen.

CONTENTS

PART II

History of Bacteriology—With Special Reference to Specific Areas

PART III

Biographical References—Bacteriologists

PART IV

Selective Guide to Biographies of Selected Bacteriologists

A GUIDE TO THE

HISTORY OF BACTERIOLOGY

INTRODUCTION*

In this so-called "age of science," history is taught seemingly about everything but science. In most universities there is at least a professor of the history of religion and one of the history of art, but rarely one of the history of science. At the present time there are only five universities in the United States where one can receive advanced training in this field; they include Brown, Cornell, Harvard, Johns Hopkins, and Wisconsin. One of the primary needs concerning the study of the history of science is simply recognition. The subject has lacked support and personnel. What we need are more modern historians of science that are men of wisdom and, in a sense, the real guardians of ideals that will aid us to understand science.

The history of science is concerned primarily with its own discipline—science itself. It will indicate man's progress with material things, his progress of understanding nature, and his development of his own consciousness, since science is based on truth. Thus, the central point of modern civilization has been the development of science, yet its history has been sadly neglected.

The historian's sacred duty is to tell of the discoveries of truth and to indicate their evolution as well as how they were transmitted and received by others. A new concept in science is seldom seen or even understood from the first presentation, at least not the whole of it. Furthermore, the great discoveries do not appear like lightning out of the sky. All have had long periods of evolution and many times the pressures for the changes are almost secret. One may see this part of it, or that, and only gradually realize the implications. In many instances the discoverers do not appreciate what they have revealed. In numerous cases so called lesser men may "carry the ball," and even these

*Introduction, taken from material from paper, Grainger, T. H. 1956. Why Study the History of Science? Improving College and University Teaching, Autumn, 79–82, by permission of the editor.

people may not understand the complete meaning until it is explained by others, perhaps teachers. For it seems to be frequently the case that only when one succeeds in explaining a truth to others is it, for the first time, understood.

It is one thing to discover a new truth, but it is also another thing to transmit it to others. Furthermore, a new idea or concept will usually meet with great resistance, for in most instances the accepted truth of the time must be proved to be incorrect. Errors, superstitions, and dogmas must be overcome or its dissemination may be stopped literally before it gets started. History of science has shown many times that the discovery of a truth is one thing, but equally necessary is its transmission to others and its acceptance. The latter are often the most difficult tasks.

Science is a becoming and not a being. It is not dead knowledge or fixed knowledge. The true scientist, as well as the historian of science, understands the present, for the past was also at one time the present. He is as interested as anyone in the latest theories, but he will usually reserve judgment about them until he has traced their evolution and has studied their history. He is not likely to be "taken in" by the latest fashion because of his historical sense. Some contemporary scientists may be prejudiced, however, and their judgments must often be corrected as much as possible by the historians of science. In some cases the experiments of the technicians, although accurate, are unfortunately so narrow or specialized that they are essentially incomplete and thus lose their significance. For one of the most important aims of science is to generalize and to simplify.

Unfortunately most people wish to be entertained as soon as history of science is mentioned. Man is always fond of anecdotes, and this probably accounts for the emphasis on the history of medicine. There have been numerous publications in this field which have been passed off as examples of histories of science. Numerous physicians are satisfied that this is really the history of science and this knowledge is all that is worthwhile.

In bacteriology, the publicity has been in medical bacteriology. This is natural, for man is most likely to be interested in the riddles of disease-producing microorganisms which affect him so often. Thus, medical bacteriology has an intensely human interest and is concerned with many aspects of social life.

Like any other subject, history has its dramatic moments, its pleasant side, and high lights, but inevitably it has interludes. The history of any branch of science, including bacteriology, should represent the whole picture, not merely fragments of the more interesting and pleasant things.

It is hard to find historians for bacteriology; there are few. Parts of its history have been written. For instance, Bulloch (1938) has written a classic entitled "The History of Bacteriology." Unfortunately the title is incorrect, as it should have been "The History of MEDICAL Bacteriology." This is, nevertheless, the most authoritative source that we have. When the history of bacteriology is finally written, Bulloch's work on medical bacteriology will have to be expanded to take into consideration the wider scope and range of bacteriology. There are not many, however, qualified for the task of writing or teaching the history of bacteriology, either the whole of it or even part of it. The historian in the field of science must have, in addition to a sound knowledge of science, philosophical wisdom and a historical sense. Even our most distinguished bacteriologists would be unqualified to write its history if they lacked these two fundamental skills. In addition, the historian of any branch of science must be able to embrace the whole picture, and his knowledge, if possible, should be tempered with justice and charity, tolerance and humility, humor and enthusiasm, beauty and simplicity.

In the United States we have too many popular articles concerning the latest "miracles" in science, mostly of a sensational nature and without great depth. The history of scientific progress in this country has been ignored for the most part, and on only a few occasions has it attracted international attention. The need for these studies has been brought to our attention by some writers for many years, but their pleas seem to have fallen too often on "deaf" ears. Writers of history of science must, however, guard against nationalistic prejudices, as for instance, "genetics" in Russia.

Our educational system in science in the United States has a tendency to hit the practical "high lights." This can be very misleading and, although it is good as far as it goes and better than nothing, it is not an education. Many people assume, for example, that our technical courses offer all that is needed in science. This assumption must be seriously questioned. Bacteriology, like many other branches of science, is known to have a high percentage of technicians. Why? One of the reasons is that technicians obviously are needed in a practical way. Some of the fault lies, however, in our educational system. We are giving many scientific courses that merely impart practical information. In many instances the course is designed with a mercenary purpose. The student may become a fine technician, but he does not educate himself. This type of course may better his financial position and may increase his usefulness, in industry for instance, but it does not enlighten him. Furthermore, the lack of enlightenment will ultimately impair his usefulness too. It seems that many of our courses in science and our educational standards in this field need re-evaluation. This indicates that administrators of science and educators have not yet appreciated the real influence of science on our civilization. Furthermore, if we wish to humanize science, one must first study its past as thoroughly as possible. It is time that something was done about adjusting our educational sights in order to inject a little of humanity into science. This can be done to a great extent in courses concerning the history and philosophy of science. These are the perspectives that give science its meaning.

If a general pronouncement in a peremptory manner is made concerning the history of bacteriology, it may well be claimed that it has rendered greater service to mankind than any other of the biological sciences. At the same time, the interpreter will point to the fact that hovering behind the atom bomb and other inventions of nuclear physics is "bacteriological warfare," the intent of which is the exact opposite for which this science has thus far been directed.

If bacteriology like other areas of science is not humanized and understood properly, it will do more harm than good. This, of course, is obviously what has happened in certain areas of applied bacteriology, for instance, in reference to possible warfare. Bacteriology can become stupid and dangerous and thus needs internal constructive criticism. It is historical, as well as philosophical study, too frequently forgotten, that would fashion our morals, ideals, and understanding of any area of science. These should then filter into the disciplines of education and forge the very needed links between science and the humanities. The existing cleavage between these disciplines could easily be minimized.

Many scientists are prejudiced or actually narrow in their outlook. Or, in some cases, they are so specialized that their truths are quite incomplete. These are often the people that reject the history of science as "irrelevant" and a waste of time. It is true that everything but tomorrow is history, and every scientist does a certain amount of retrospection. But usually his work brings him in contact with the past works of predecessors in only a very superficial way. This can sometimes be a source of much error. To these people, if the scientific ideas and data are older than the current journals, attention to them appears a waste of time. Yet it is almost impossible for contemporary workers to be unprejudiced, and it is difficult indeed not to make mistakes. Historians in their better position will probably correct them. But at least the educated scientist will attempt to make modern judgments in the light of history and with the hope that in the cold light of posterity the dispassionate judgments of his work may be favorable. Thus many scientists, due to our technological specialized society, have little vision for larger relationships. The only way to overcome this narrow outlook is to provide historical perspectives. Broader outlooks are needed because technology has advanced far more rapidly than our contemplative adjustments. One of the functions of a study of the history of science is to illuminate other fields such as the social sciences and humanities. Much of the work will serve as a source for other scholars. The social relations of science can only be obtained, for instance, after its history has been written.

In too many places, however, the borderline nature of the discipline, history of science, falls between two schools. The history department relegates it to the scientist, while the science division assigns it to the historians. Other factors may also be involved. For instance, some general historians appreciate the impact of science on society but are unable to deal with the technical language, or lack a sound background in science for an understanding.

Thus the study of the history of bacteriology, although admittedly sadly neglected, offers great potential values to science and education. It is this study that exhibits the sense, purpose, and reasoning of bacteriology. To understand its conception and evolution is what makes it worthwhile and interesting. The study of the history of any branch of science, in general, will aid us to find the truth. It will teach us to appreciate the present benefiting from the researches of the past and will instruct us in the defense of tradition. It will school us to criticize bacteriology constructively and with understanding. It will teach us humility.

It will show us the needs and problems and will give us a deeper interpretation of bacteriology. It will help us to some extent to bridge the difference between the humanities and science. It will enlighten modern general historians. It will aid our moral outlook toward mankind. Furthermore, one will find, also, that it is a most welcome and enjoyable diversion.

Perhaps it is possible to stimulate or at least point to the desired need for this interest in bacteriology. The history of this branch of science is certainly not too big and one should be able to encompass the whole of it. To this end, the objective of this bibliography is to serve as a broad guide to the literature of bacteriology to aid those who will teach the history of bacteriology.

Part I

SELECTIVE GUIDE TO THE LITERATURE
OF BACTERIOLOGY

Abstracts, bibliographies, indexes, etc., may have some secondary value or may serve as mere indicators to the history of bacteriology. It should be emphasized that the current abstracting journals are able to analyze only about 10–15 per cent of the world's literature. See, Sarton's Guide (Horus), pp. 105–110, for other abstracting and review journals for broad coverage or other subjects:

1. Sarton, G. 1952. Horus. A guide to the history of science. A Chronica Botanica Publication. The Ronald Press Co., New York. 316 pp.

A. General References

1

BIBLIOGRAPHIES, INDEXES, ABSTRACTS

Comprehensive, but most are of limited value in bacteriology. The following list is merely selective:

2. **Artelt, W.** 1953. **Index zur Geschichte der Medizin, Naturwissenschaft und Technik. Vol. 1.** Urban und Schwarzenberg, München und Berlin. 398 pp. Reviewed by Pagel, W. 1954. Isis, 45, 109. This is a tremendous collection of 7,022 works of medical, 182 of dental, 374 of pharmaceutical, 2,292 of scientific and technological, and 751 of biological history for the years 1945–1948. Much of the German literature which appeared during the war and early post-war period is now being made known. This publication is intended to close the gap caused by the cessation of Mitteilungen zur Geschichte der Medizin, der Naturwissenschaft und der Technik during the war. Several special chapters, e.g., Hygiene, Epidemiologie, Bakteriologie, Öffentliches Gesundheitswesen, pp. 206–214. Source of indexes, etc., p. 28.

3. **Besterman, T.** 1947. **A world bibilography of bibliographies.** 2d ed. Privately published by the author, Theodore Besterman, London. 3d ed. 4 vols. UNESCO, Geneva. See section on bacteria, etc.

4. **Bibliografia Italiana.** 1928–1943. Consiglio Nazionale della Ricerche, Section A bis Biologia; B Medicina. Brief annotations or abstracts.

5. **Bibliographic Index.** 1945. Vol. 1, 1937–1942; vol. 2., 1943–1946. A cumulative bibliography of bibliographies. H. W. Wilson Co., New York. See section on bacteria, etc. Of very limited value to the bacteriologist.

6. **Biblioteca Scientifica Sovietica.** 1949-date. Instituto Bibliografico Italiano Rome. Section "Biologia e Medicina," is extensive.
7. **British Abstracts.** 1882-n.b. Title varies. Part A. III, includes biochemistry, pharmacology (1953), experimental medicine, microbiology, pathology, and physiology. Continued in 1954 by British Abstracts of Medical Sciences.
8. **Centre National de la Recherche Scientifique.** 1940–date. Bulletin analytique. The Centre, Paris. Part I includes microscopy. Part 2, the biological sciences. Brief annotations.
9. **Crane, E. J., Patterson, A. M., and Marr, E. B.** 1957. A guide to the literature of chemistry. 2d ed. John Wiley & Sons, Inc., New York. 397 pp. Lists indexes, abstracts, journals, books, etc. A very valuable guide for bacteriologists interested in the chemical aspects of bacteriology.
10. **Doe, J., and Marshall, M. L.** (eds.). 1956. Medical library practice. 2d ed. American Library Assoc., Chicago. 601 pp. Note list of bibliographies, pp. 349–350. Section on bacteriology, viruses, etc., pp. 422–424
11. **The Educational Index.** Vol. 1, 1932–date. A cumulative author and subject index to a selected list of educational periodicals, books, and pamphlets, 1929–date. H. W. Wilson Co., New York. Covers a few periodicals of interest to bacteriologists.
12. **Engineering Index.** 1884–date. Engineering Index, Inc., New York. Of some interest to early work of sanitary and engineering aspects of bacteriology. Especially good on water purification and water supplies.
13. **FIAT Review of German Science.** 1939–1946. Published by the Office of Military Government for Germany; Field Information Agencies Technical, British, French, U. S.; printed under the supervision of Dieterich'scheVerlagsbuchhandlung, Inhaber W. Klemm. Vol. 64–65, Bacteriology and virus diseases. 1950, English translation.
14. **Fleming, T. P.** 1952. Guide to the literature of science. Columbia University, School of Library Service, New York. Mimeographed, 46 pp. Lists indexes, abstracts, etc.
15. **Hassall, A.** *et al.* 1932. Index-catalogue of medical and veterinary zoology. Government Printing Office, Washington, D. C. Supplement, 1953. A revision and continuation of 1st ed. of Stiles and Hassall.

16. Hirshberg, H. S., and Melinat, C. H. 1947. Subject guide to
    United States government publications. American Library
    Assoc., Chicago.
17. Industrial Arts Index. 1913–date. H. W. Wilson Co., New
    York. Monthly sections cumulate every few months, ulti-
    mately appearing in 2-year bound volume. Of limited value.
    Duplicates much of material in Engineering Index.
18. International Catalogue of Scientific Literature. 1902–1921.
    Published for the International Council of Scientific
    Workers by the Royal Society of London, London. Section
    R, bacteriology. Extensive coverage of earlier literature.
19. Internationale Bibliographie der Bibliographien. 1950.
    Vittorio Klostermann, Frankfort am Main. 652 pp. Section
    Gesundheitspflege u. Bakteriologie, pp. 485–487.
20. Ireland, N. O. 1942. An index to indexes. The R. W. Faxon
    Co., Boston. A very limited and selective list.
21. Japan Science Review. 1954. Vol. 1, ed. by the Science
    Council of Japan and the Ministry of Education, Tokyo,
    Japan. Medical sciences, bibliography, and abstracts.
    Abstracts in English of all the more important medical re-
    search.
22. Jenkins, F. B. 1954. University of Illinois. Library School,
    Science reference sources; a selected list of titles for use
    in Library Science 412. Illini Union Bookstore, Champaign,
    Ill. Includes section for microbiology.
23. Monthly Catalogue of United States Government Publications.
    1895–date. Issued by the Superintendent of Documents,
    U. S. Government Printing Office, Washington, D. C.
24. National Research Council of Egypt. 1951–date. Classified
    list of Egyptian scientific papers. The Council, Cairo.
    Arabic titles translated.
25. Public Affairs Information Service. 1915–date. Public
    Affairs Press, New York. Cites selected pamphlets,
    government publications, books, annuals, periodical
    articles.
26. Science Abstracts. 1898–date. Physical Soc. London,
    Amer. Phy. Soc. and Institution of Electrical Engineers,
    London. Section A; of interest only in a very specific
    feature, i.e., physics abstracts, electron microscope.
27. Stiles, C. W., and Hassall, A. 1920–1950. Index-catalogue
    of medical and veterinary zoology. Authors, A–Z. U. S.
    Bureau of Animal Industry, Bulletin No. 39. Government

Printing Office, Washington, D. C. A fine bibliography based chiefly on the card catalogs of the Bureau of Animal Industry and the Hygiene Laboratory. Of limited value in bacteriology.

28. **Svenska Institutet för Kulturellt Utbyte med Utlandet,** Stockholm, 1949. Swedish books and publications on science, medicine, and the humanities. 1939–1947. Swedish Institute, Stockholm. 199 pp.

29. **Technical Libraries, Their Organization and Management.** 1951. Ed. by Jackson, L. Special Libraries Assoc., New York. Excellent appendix with important lists of reference publications and specimen subject field bibliographies. Microbiology included, pp. 62–63.

30. **United Nations Educational, Scientific, and Cultural Organization.** Science Cooperation Office (Latin America), Montevideo. List of scientific papers published in Latin America. 1949–date. Includes biology and medicine but is incomplete. Science Cooperation Office (Middle East). 1947–date. Cairo. List of scientific papers published in the Middle East (Afghanistan, Cyprus, Syria, and Turkey). Annotations in French or English. Excellent coverage on medicine but irregular. Science Cooperation Office (South Asia). 1949–date. Delhi, India. Bibliography of scientific publications of South Asia (India, Burma, Ceylon). Includes a descriptive list of serials of South Asia. Extensive coverage on medicine.

31. **Winchell, C. M.** 1951. Guide to reference books. 7th ed. American Library Assoc., Chicago. 645 pp. Supplement, 1954. Winchell, C. M., and Johnson, O. A. 117 pp. Supplement, 1956. Winchell, C. M. Note excellent listing of bibliographies, periodicals, special section on bacteriology, etc.

2

GOVERNMENT DOCUMENTS

Excellent check lists for government publications of foreign countries as well as the United States are found in:

41. Crane, E. J., Patterson, A. M., and Marr, E. B. 1957. A guide to the literature of chemistry. John Wiley & Sons, Inc., New York. pp. 183–198.
42. Doe, J., and Marshall, M. L. 1956. Medical library practice. American Library Assoc., Chicago. Pp. 357–358.
43. Winchell, C. M. 1951. Guide to reference books. 7th ed. American Library Assoc., Chicago. Pp. 105–110. Supplement, 1954. Winchell, C. M., and Johnson, O. A. Pp. 18–20. Supplement, 1956. Winchell, C. M.

3

HISTORY OF BIOLOGY

See listings by:

53. Morton, L. T. 1954. Garrison and Morton's medical bibliography. An annotated check-list of texts illustrating the history of medicine. 2d ed. Printed by W. J. Rawlinson, Ltd., Netherlands. Pp. 10–15.
54. Sarton, G. 1952. Horus. A guide to the history of science. A Chronica Botanica Publication. The Ronald Press Co., New York. Pp. 171–173.

4

HISTORY OF SCIENCE

64. Russo, F. 1954. Histoire des Sciences et des Techniques. Bibliographie. Herman & Cie, Éditeurs, Paris. 186 pp. Excellent check list, bibliography, and emphasis on technology. Reviewed by Sarton, G. 1954. Isis, 45, 204–205. Professor George Sarton advises "historians of Science to keep Russo and his guide 'Horus' close together on their first-aid shelf."
65. Sarton, G. 1952. Horus. A guide to the history of science. A Chronica Botanica Publication. The Ronald Press Co.,

New York. 316 pp. By far the most comprehensive source. Outstanding. See listing of numerous reviews. 1953 Isis, 44, 91–93; 1955 Isis, 46, 115.

Although the above guides are excellent for the broad coverage of science, they are very poor for the field of bacteriology.

List of journals dealing with the history of science:

66. **Biological Sciences Serial Publications.** A world list, 1950–1954. 1955. Biological Abstracts, Philadelphia. Pp. 192–193.

5

MEDICAL ABSTRACTS, INDEXES, ETC.

The following references are extremely valuable for their fine listings and guides that are in some instances of interest to medical bacteriologists.

76. **Doe, J.,** and **Marshall, M. L.** 1956. Medical library practice. 2d ed. American Library Assoc., Chicago. Pp. 358–365. An excellent listing with annotations.
77. **Morton, L. T.** 1954. Garrison and Morton's medical bibliography. 2d ed. Argosy Bookstore, New York. Note excellent listing of medical bibliography, pp. 584–588.
78. **Winchell, C. M.** 1951. Guide to reference books. 7th ed. American Library Assoc., Chicago. Pp. 319–328. Supplement, 1954. Winchell, C. M., and Johnson, O. A. Pp. 58–59. The above publications are outstanding and should be available for all reference purposes.

In addition, the following publication is also valuable:

79. **Pauley, A.** 1954. Bibliographie des Sciences Médicales. Derek Verschoyle. Academic and Bibliographical Publications, Ltd., London. It comprises an exhaustive bibliography of the history of various branches of medicine, epidemics, and disease, as well as medical and professional literature.

Although the following two publications are listed in the first three above-mentioned guides, it is perhaps well to emphasize their importance again:

80. **Current List of Medical Literature.** 1941–date. National Library of Medicine, U. S. Department of Health, Education and Welfare. Public Health Service, Washington, D. C. (Government Printing Office, Washington, D. C.) Tables of contents of current journals. Supplemental check for current year.

81. **Index-Catalogue of the Library of the Surgeon General's Office—United States Army.** 1880–date. Army Medical Library, Government Printing Office, Washington, D. C. Note excellent sections on bacteriology, etc.

Also see, **Abstracts—Bacteriology.**

6

MEDICAL ADVANCES, ANNALS, ARCHIVES, ETC.

There are numerous special areas in medicine that may be of interest to the medical bacteriologist. For example: allergy, antibiotics, cancer, dentistry, endocrinology, food and nutrition, industrial medicine and hygiene, laboratories, metabolism, nursing, pathology, pharmacology and pharmacy, physiology, public health, epidemiology, sanitation, tropical medicine, and veterinary medicine. There are also other areas, such as biology, botany and agriculture, chemistry and biochemistry, enzymology, genetics and eugenics, microscopy, mycology, physics, parasitology, ultrasonics, and viruses.

In addition there are infectious diseases that are of interest, such as: cholera, leprosy, plague, poliomyelitis, smallpox, tuberculosis, yellow fever, etc.

An excellent listing of these publications with annotations is found in:

91. **Crane, E. J., Patterson, A. M., and Marr, E. B.** 1957. A guide to the literature of chemistry. John Wiley & Sons, Inc., New York. Pp. 206–212.

92. Doe, J., and Marshall, M. L. 1956. Medical library practice. Amer. Library Assoc., Chicago. Pp. 412-537.

7

REFERENCE WORKS

The following references are useful in every scientific institution and library:

102. Index Generalis, 1954-1955. 1955. Annuaire Général des Universités, des Bibliothèques, Instituts Scientifiques, Musées, Observatoires, Sociétés Savantes, etc. Paris. 2064 pp. Also English edition.
103. The International Who's Who, 1955. 19th edition. London. 1098 pp. Most useful and most exhaustive of reference books, giving an immense wealth of accurate information about the leading personalities in the world today.
104. The World of Learning, 1955. London. 1038 pp. An indispensable guide to scientific, cultural, and educational life in all parts of the world. It gives much detailed information about learned societies, libraries, museums, universities, colleges, and technical institutions throughout the world.

8

SCIENTIFIC AWARDS

Prizes in history of science, see:

114. Sarton, G. 1952. Horus. A guide to the history of science. A Chronica Botanica Publication. The Ronald Press Co., New York. P. 303.

See also:

115. The Blue Book of Awards. 1956. Published by Marquis. Who's Who, Chicago, Ill. 186 pp.

116. Firth, M. A. 1956. Handbook of scientific and technical
     awards in the United States and Canada, 1900-1952.
     Special Libraries Assoc., New York. 491 pp.

9

SOURCES OF PATENT INFORMATION

126. Crane, E. J., Patterson, A. M., and Marr, E. B. 1957. A
     guide to the literature of chemistry. John Wiley & Sons,
     Inc., New York. A chapter is devoted to the scope and
     sources of patent information, pp. 158-182. This is in-
     ternational in its range and is one of the best condensed
     sources available.

10

SOURCES OF RESEARCH SUPPORT

     See:

136. Wolfle, D. 1957. Sources of research support. Science,
     125, 97. This is an excellent short editorial which gives
     valuable information concerning American foundations,
     etc.

B. References on Bacteriology

11

ABSTRACTS

146. Abstracts of Bacteriology. 1917-1925. Williams & Wilkins
     Co., Baltimore, Md. Bimonthly 1917-1920; monthly 1921-

1925; 9 vols. Published by the Society of American Bacteriologists. Merged with "Botanical Abstracts" and expanded to create "Biological Abstracts."

147. **Abstracts of Bacteriology.** 1917. A list of periodicais to
be reviewed in abstracts of bacteriology. Abs. Bact.,
1, 3–24.

148. **Abstracts of Papers.** International Congress for Microbiology. 1930; every 3 years. International Association of
Microbiologists. Abstracts and proceedings of con-
gresses. Text in English, French, or Portuguese.

149. **Biological Abstracts.** 1926–date. Union of American
Biological Societies, Univ. of Pennsylvania, Philadelphia, Pa. Subject index or systematic index. Section
C on microbiology. Includes immunology, bacteriology,
viruses, protozoology, and helminthology. Papers and
books on the history of biology are abstracted in the
general section. Obituaries of biologists are also listed
by title and place of publication.

150. **Bulletin de l'Institut Pasteur.** 1903–date. Masson et Cie,
Paris. Revues et analyses des travaux de bactériologie
et de médecine, biologie générale, physiologie, chimie
biologique dans leurs rapports avec la microbiologie.
Classified by subject and especially good for foreign
literature.

151. **Chemical Abstracts.** 1907–date. Easton, Pa. Section 11C,
Microbiology. Most comprehensive of abstract journals.
Excellent for bacteriologists and in many instances superior to biological abstracts in certain specific areas
of bacteriology.

152. **Chemisches Zentralblatt; Vollständiges Repertorium für
alle Zweige der Reinen und Angewandten Chemie.** 1830–
date. Berlin. Classified subject index under Mikroben,
Mikroorganismen, etc.

153. **Dairy Science Abstracts.** 1939–date. Reading, England.
Abstracts, analyses, and book reviews.

154. **Ergebnisse der Hygiene, Bakteriologie, Immunitätsforschung
und Experimentellen Pharmakilogie.** 1914–date.
Begründet von Wolfgang Weichardt, ed. by Doerr, R., und
Schlorsberger, H. Vol. 29, 1955. Berlin. Suspended
1944–1948. Continuation of Jahresbericht über die
Ergebnisse der Immunitätsforschung. Reviews with good
bibliographies.

155. **Excerpta Medica.** 1947–date. Amsterdam, The Netherlands. Williams & Wilkins Co., Baltimore. Section IV, Medical microbiology, immunology, and serology. Section II, Physiology, biochemistry and pharmacology, antibiotics, antiseptics. Text in English.

156. **Index Medicus.** Series I, vols. 1–21. 1879–1899. Changed to: Bibliographia medica, 1900–1902; Index medicus, Series II, vols. 1–18. 1903–1920. War supplement, 1914–1917. Index medicus, Series III, vols. 1–6. 1921–1926. Quarterly cumulative index, 1916–1926. Quarterly cumulative index medicus, 1926–date. American Medical Society, Chicago.

157. Jahresbericht über die Fortschritte in der Lehre von den Gärungs-Organismen und Enzymen. 1891–1916. Leipzig. Covers the period 1890–1911. Edited by Koch, A. Classified abstracts of literature on physiology of bacteria, fermentation, nutrition. Arranged by subjects, but bibliographic information often incomplete.

158. Jahresbericht über die Fortschritte in der Lehre von den pathogenen Mikroorganismen umfassend Bakterien, Pilze und Protozoen. 1885–1911. Vols. 1–27. Braunschweig, Leipzig. Ed. by Baumgarten, P. Includes theses. Cumulative index, vols. 1–10. No more published.

159. Jahresbericht über die Ergebnisse der Immunitätsforschung. 1905–1912. Stuttgart. Abstract journal superseded by Ergebnisse der Hygiene, ... 8 vols. Classified index to articles on immunity. Each volume contains one or two review articles on special topics.

160. Japanese Journal of Medical Sciences. 1929–date. Thirteen sections, including Section VI, Bacteriology and Parasitology. Abstract portion arranged chronologically. Gives data from otherwise inaccessible Japanese literature. English or German abstracts of the Japanese medical literature.

161. **Mikrobiologiia.** 1932–date. Akademiia Nauk SSSR, Moscow. Bimonthly. Also includes original research, analyses, and book reviews.

162. **Milchwissenschaft;** Internationale Forschungsberichte und Nachrichten aus der Gesamten Milchwirtschaft für Wissenshaft und Praxis. 1946–date. Nuremberg, Germany. Also includes original research and analyses. Occasional articles in English. Summaries in English, French, German, and Spanish.

163. **N.A.A.S.** Quarterly Review; The Journal of the National Agriculture Advisory Service. 1949–date. London. Also includes analyses.

164. **Nutrition Abstracts and Reviews.** 1931–date. Commonwealth Bureau of Animal Nutrition. Reid Library and Royett Institute, Aberdeen, Scotland. For growth requirements of bacteria and other microorganisms; synthesis of vitamins, pigments, bacterial flora, and problems of various food products.

165. **Prevention of Deterioration Abstracts.** 1945. National Research Council, Prevention of Deterioration Center, Ottawa, Canada. Issued in loose-leaf folders by National Research Council. Section on biological agents, fungicides, and other toxic compounds, deterioration of paints, piling, fabrics, paper, etc.

166. **Prevention of Deterioration Abstracts.** 1946–date. National Research Council, Washington, D. C.

167. Sovetskoe Meditsinskoe Referativnoe Obozrenie: Mikrobiologiia, Infektsionnye Bolezni, Epidemiologiia. 1948–date. Moscow. Medical abstracts: microbiology, epidemiology, and infectious diseases. Abstracts from world literature. Three numbers/yr.

168. **Tsentral'nyi Referativnyi Meditsinskii Zhurnal.** 1928–date. Moscow. Subdivided vol. 21 (1938) into 4 parts, of which, Seriya G: Mikrobiologiya gigiena i sanitariya, epidemologiya, etc. (Microbiology of health and sanitation, aviation medicine, etc.). Classified abstracts, review articles, and occasional bibliographies in Russian.

169. **U. S. Office of Naval Research.** 1953. Vol. 1. Progress report abstracts, Microbiology Branch. Department of Navy, Washington, D. C.

170. **Zentralblatt für Bakteriologie, Parasitenkunde und Infektionskrankheiten und Hygiene.** 1887–date. Jena. Abteilung I. Medizinisch-Hygienische Bakteriologie, Virusforschung und tierische Parasitologie. Monthly, 2 vols./yr. Vols. 1–30, 1887–1901, contain both original papers and Referate (classified abstracts) mingled together in one volume, hence are difficult to use as bibliographies. Beginning with vol. 31 (1902) Referate issued separately. Includes literature on infectious diseases, chemotherapy, disinfection, tumors, veterinary medicine, protozoology, and helminthology. Abteilung II Allge-

meine landwirtschaftliches, technische, usw. Covers
agricultural, tanning, fermentation, nutritional aspects,
etc. Extensive coverage, especially of European literature. Also includes original research. Includes virology.

171. Zentralblatt für die gesamte Hygiene mit Einschluss der
Bakteriologie und Immunitätslehre. 1922–date. Berlin.
Comprehensive abstract journal; successor to Hygien-
ische Rundschau, with particularly good coverage of
foreign literature. Extensive bibliography on infectious
diseases and their control.

172. Zhurnal Mikrobiologii, Epidemiologii I Immunobiologii.
1924–date. Ministerstvo Zdravookhraneniia SSSR, Moscow. Microbiology, epidemiology, and immunobiology.
Original research, analyses, abstracts, book reviews,
news notes, bibliographies.

12

ANALYSES* (INCLUDING REVIEW LITERATURE AND SUMMARIES OF ORIGINAL RESEARCH)

182. Acta Microbiologica Polonica; Microbiologia Generalis,
Agrobiologia et Technica. 1952–date. Warsaw, Poland.
Text in Polish; summaries in English and Russian. Quar-
terly. Also bibliographies.

183. Acta Pathologica et Microbiologica Scandinavica. 1924–
date. Copenhagen, Denmark. Text in English, French,
or German; summaries in English. Eight times a year.
Also original research.

184. Acta Physiologica Academiae Scientiarum Hungaricae.
1950–irregular. Budapest, Hungary. Text in English,
French, German, or Russian; summaries in various languages. Also original research and proceedings of
societies.

185. Advances in Virus Research. 1953–date. Academic Press,
Inc., New York. Annual.

*Based on listings from Biological Sciences Serial Publica-
tions. A World List, 1950–1954. 1955. Biological Abstracts,
Philadelphia.

186. Annales de l'Institut Pasteur. 1887–date. Masson et Cie, Paris. Text in English or French. Also original research, proceedings, and *Séances de la Société Française de Microbiologie*.
187. Annales de l'Institut Pasteur de Lille. 1948–date. Paris. Also original research.
188. Annali (di) Microbiologia. Memorie di microbiologia generale ed applicata alla agricoltura, alle industrie fermentative ed alimentari; di enzimologia e chimica della fermentazioni nei loro rapporti con la microbiologia e la batteriologia industriale. 1940–irregular. Milan.
189. Annual Report. Hannah Dairy Research Institute. 1932–date. Kirkhill, Scotland.
190. Annual Review of Microbiology. 1947–date. Annual Reviews, Inc., Stanford, Calif.
191. Antonie van Leeuwenhoek; Journal of Microbiology and Serology. 1934–date. Amsterdam, Netherlands. Text in English, French, or German. Four times a year. Also original research.
192. Arbeiten aus dem Sero-Bakteriologischen Institut der Universitat Helsinki. 1928–date. Helsinki, Finland. Text in English or German; occasional summaries in other languages. Also original research and collected reprints.
193. Archiv für die Gesamte Virusforschung. 1949–irregular. Springer-Verlag, Vienna. Also original research.
194. Archiv für Hygiene und Bakteriologie; Forschungsarbeiten aus Hygiene und Mikrobiologie Einschliesslich Öffentlicher Gesundheitspflege, Gewerbehygiene und Sozialhygiene. 1883–irregular. Munich, Germany. Summaries in English, French, and German. Also original research.
195. Archiv für Mikrobiologie; Zeitschrift für die Erforschung des pflanzlichen Mikroorganismen. 1930–irregular. Berlin. Occasional articles in English. Also original research.
196. Archives d'Anatomie Microscopique et de Morphologie Expérimentale. 1897–date. Paris. Also original research. Quarterly.
197. Archives de l'Institut d'Hessarek. 1939–irregular. Teheran, Iran.
198. Archives de l'Institut Pasteur d'Algérie. 1923–date. Algiers. Also original research. Quarterly.
199. Archives de l'Institut Pasteur de la Guyane. 1951–date. Cahors, France. Also includes original research, the

Institute's publications, and *rapport sur le Fonctionne-ment Technique*.

200. Archives de l'Institut Pasteur de la Martinique. 1948–date. Cahors, France. Semiannual.

201. Archives de l'Institut Pasteur de Tananarive; Extrait du Rapport Annuel. 1932–date. Tananarive, Madagascar.

202. Archives de l'Institut Pasteur du Maroc. 1932–irregular. Casablanca, French Morocco. Also original research.

203. Archives de l'Institut Pasteur Hellenique, Nouvelle Série. 1955–date. Athens, Greece. Text in French or Greek; Greek papers have summaries in French. Quarterly.

204. Arquivos do Instituto Bacteriológica Câmara Pestana. 1906–irregular. Text in French or Portugese; summaries in English. Also original research.

205. Bacteriological Reviews. 1937–date. Baltimore, Md. Also original research. Quarterly.

206. Bollettino (della) Societa Italiana di Microbiologia. 1929–1934. Milan.

207. Bollettino Dell'Instituto Sieroterapico Milanese; Archivio di Microbiologia ed Immunologia. 1917–date. Milan, Italy. Text in Italian; summaries in English and Italian. Also original research. Bimonthly.

208. Bulletin (de l') Association des Diplômés de Microbiologie de la Faculté de Pharmacie de Nancy. 1931–date. Nancy.

209. Ceskoslovenska Hygiena; Epidemiologie; Mikrobiologie. 1952–date. Prague, Czechoslovakia. Text in Czech; summaries in German and Russian. Six times a year.

210. *Communications du Laboratoire Bactériologique de l'Etat Suédois; Meddelanden Från Statens Bakteriologiske Laboratorium. Date? Stockholm, Sweden. Text in English, French, or Swedish; Swedish papers have occasional summaries in other languages. Also original research.

211. Dairy Science Abstracts. 1939–date. Reading, England. Also abstracts and book reviews.

212. Ergebnisse der Hygiene, Bakteriologie, Immunitätsforschung und Experimentellen Therapie. 1914–irregular. Berlin. Also original research.

213. Giornale di Batteriologia e Immunologia. 1917–date. Torino, Italy. Also original research.

*Items marked with an asterisk indicate that the original has not been seen.

214. International Bulletin of Bacteriological Nomenclature and
     Taxonomy. 1951-date. Ames, Iowa.

215. Izvestiia na Mikrobiologicheskiia Institut; Bulletin de l'In-
     stitut de Microbiologie de l'Académie Bulgare des Scien-
     ces. 1950-date. Sofia, Bulgaria. Text in Bulgarian;
     summaries in French and Russian.

216. The Journal of Applied Bacteriology. 1945-irregular.
     Reading, England. Also original research and proceed-
     ings. Title changed from "The Proceedings of the So-
     ciety for Applied Bacteriology," April, 1954.

217. Journal of Bacteriology. 1916-date. Baltimore, Md. Mainly
     original research.

218. The Journal of Dairy Research. 1929-date. Cambridge,
     London. Also original research. Three times a year.

219. The Journal of Pathology and Bacteriology. 1892-date.
     London. Also, original research and proceedings of
     societies.

220. Journal of the New Zealand Association of Bacteriologists.
     1946-date. Auckland, New Zealand. Three times a year.

221. Materialy k Miobibliografii Uchenykh USSR, Seriia Biolo-
     gisheskikh Nauk: Mikrobiologia. 1947-date. Moscow.
     Biobibliography in microbiology. Numbered monographic
     series.

222. Medycyna Doswiadczalna I Mikrobiologia. 1949-date. War-
     saw, Poland. Also original research. Quarterly.

223. Microbiologia Espanola. 1947-date. Madrid.

224. The Micropaleontologist. 1947-date. New York. Also
     news notes. Quarterly.

225. Mikrobiologichnyi Zhurnal. 1934-date. Kiev, USSR. Also
     original research. Quarterly.

226. Mikrobiologiia. 1932-date. Moscow. Also original re-
     search, abstracts, book reviews. Excellent for soil,
     water, applications to agriculture.

227. Mikrobiologji Dergisi; Revue de Microbiologie. 1948-date.
     Istambul, Turkey. Text in Turkish; summaries in English
     or French. Also proceedings of societies. Quarterly.

228. Mikrokosmos; Zeitschrift für Angewandte Mikroskopie,
     Mikrobiologie, Mikrochemie und Mikroskropische Technik.
     1907-date. Stuttgart, Germany. Also original research,
     book reviews, news notes.

229. Milchwissenschaft; Internationale Forschungsberichte und
     Nachrichten aus der Gesamten Milchwirtschaft für Wis-

senschaft und Praxis. 1946–date. Nuremberg, Germany. Occasional articles in English; summaries in English, French, German, and Spanish. Also original research and abstracts.

230. Mitteilungen aus dem Gebeite der Lebensmitteluntersuchung und Hygiene; Travaux de Chimie Alimentaire et d'Hygiène; Offizielles Organ der Schweizerischen Gesellschaft für Analytische und Angewandte Chemie. 1910–date. Bern, Switzerland. Text in French or German; summaries in English, French, and German. Also proceedings of societies and book reviews.

231. Mitteilungen aus dem Institut für Biochemische Technologie und Lebensmittelchemie der Technischen Hochschule in Graz. 1947–date. Graz, Austria. Biennial.

232. N.A.A.S. Quarterly Review; The Journal of the National Agricultural Advisory Service. 1949–date. London. Also abstracts. Quarterly.

233. Publications. Institut Pasteur de la Guyane. Cahors, France. 1940–irregular. Also original research. Monographic series; a subseries of the Institute's "Archives," beginning January, 1951.

234. Pure Culture Study of Bacteria. 1932–1950. Geneva, N. Y. Semiannual. Ceased publication.

235. *Rapport sur le Fonctionnement Technique. Institut Pasteur de Saigon. 1950?–date. Saigon, Indochina.

236. *Rapport sur le Fonctionnement Technique de l'Institut Pasteur de Brazzaville. Date? Laval, France.

237. *Rapport sur le Fonctionnement Technique de l'Institut Pasteur de l'Afrique Occidentale Française. Date? Sénégal, French West Africa.

238. *Revue de Microbiologie Appliquée à l'Agriculture, à l'Hygiène, à l'Industrie. Date? Paris, France.

239. Schweizerische Zeitschrift für Allgemeine Pathologie und Bakteriologie; Revue Suisse de Pathologie Générale et de Bacteriologie; Swiss Journal of General Pathology and Bacteriology. 1938–date. Basel, Switzerland. Text in French or German; summaries in English, French, German, and Italian. Also original research, book reviews, proceedings of societies. Bimonthly.

240. Travaux du Laboratoire de Microbiologie de la Faculté de Pharmacie de Nancy. 1928–date. Nancy, France. Also original research.

241. Trudove na Mikrobiologicheskiia Institut. 1950–irregular.
     Sofia, Bulgaria. Text in Bulgarian, summaries in French.
     Monographic series. Also original research.
242. *Trudy Instituta Mikrobiologii. 1951? Moscow. Also origi-
     nal research.
243. Trudy Vsesoiuznogo Nauchno-Issledovatel'skogo Instituta
     Sel'skokhoziaistvennoi Mikrobiologii. 1949–date.
     Moscow. Also original research.
244. Turkish Bulletin of Hygiene and Experimental Biology;
     Türk Ijiyen ve Tecrübî Biyoloji Dergisi. 1941-irregular.
     Ankara, Turkey. Text in English, German, or Turkish;
     Turkish papers have summaries in English. Also original
     research.
245. Zeitschrift für Immunitätsforschung und Experimentelle
     Therapie. 1908–date. Stuttgart, Germany. Also original
     research. Quarterly.
246. Zeitschrift für Zellforschung und Mikroskopische Anatomie.
     1924-irregular. Berlin. Also original research.
247. Zhurnal Mikrobiologii, Epidemiologii I Immunobiologii.
     1924–date. Moscow. Also original research, abstracts,
     book reviews, news notes, bibliographies.

     Also see **Abstracts—Bacteriology.**

13

BACTERIAL CULTURES—CATALOGS

257. American Type Culture Collection. 1949. Catalogue of
     cultures. 5th ed. Washington, D. C. Supplement, 1952.
258. Annual Report. International Federation of Culture Collec-
     tions of Microorganisms. N. Y. State Department of
     Health, Division of Laboratories and Research, Albany.
     Annual.
259. British Commonwealth Collections of Microorganisms.
     1951. Directory of collections and lists of species main-
     tained in the United Kingdom and Crown Colonies.
     H.M.S.O., London. (1956—Directory of collections and
     list of species maintained in Canada.)
260. Cowan, S. T. 1951. United Kingdom Culture Collections.
     Jour. Gen. Microbiol., 5, 605–607.

261. Information Bulletin. Centre de Collection de Types Microbiens. 1947? International Federation of Culture Collections of Microorganisms. Lausanne, Switzerland.
262. Report. 1947. Specialist conference on culture collections of microorganisms. S. O. Code No. 47–139. H.M.S.O., London.

Also numerous private organizations.

14

BOOK REVIEWS—CONTEMPORARY

272. Acta Microbiologica Polonica; Microbiologia Generalis, Agrobiologia et Technica.
273. American Public Health Journal. Lists books and some reviews.
274. Antibiotics & Chemotherapy.
275. Antonie van Leeuwenhoek; Journal of Microbiology and Serology.
276. Archives of Biochemistry and Biophysics.
277. Athens; Rassegna Mensile di Biologia—Clinica e Terapia.
278. Biochimica et Biophysica Acta; . . .
279. The Bulletin of Mathematical Biophysics.
280. Chemical and Engineering News. Annotated book list.
281. French Bibliographical Digest. Special section on microbiology.
282. Giornale di Batteriologie e Immunologia.
283. Isis. The unequaled example of outstanding reviews. Tremendous coverage. See numerous volumes for catalogs of second-hand books on the history and philosophy of science.
284. Izvestiia na Mikrobiologicheskiia Institut; Buletin de l'Institut de Microbiologie de l'Académie Bulgare des Sciences.
285. Journal de Chimie—Physique et de Physico-Chimie Biologique.
286. Journal of Histochemistry and Cytochemistry.
287. Journal of the Franklin Institute.
288. Journal Pathology & Bacteriology. Excellent reviews.

289. **Mikrobiologiia.** Akademiia Naul SSSR, Moscow.
290. **Mikrokosmos;** Zeitschrift für Angewandte Mikroskopie, Mikrobiologie, Mikrochemie und Mikroskropische Technik.
291. **Mitteilungen aus dem Gebeite der Lebensmitteluntersuchung und Hygiene;** ...
292. **Nature.** Excellent reviews, international in scope.
293. **News Letter.** Soc. American Bacteriologists. Unfortunately very incomplete.
294. **Notiziario dell'Instituto Vaccinogeno Antitubercolare.**
295. **Pharmazeutische Zentralhalle für Deutschland.**
296. **Die Pharmazie;** ...
297. **Quarterly Review Biology.** Extensive coverage with outstanding reviews.
298. **Revista de la Asociación Bioquímica Argentina.**
299. **Revista Dell'Instituto Sieroterapico Italiano.**
300. **Schweizerische Zeitschrift für Allgemeine Pathologie und Bakteriologie;** ...
301. **Science.** Weekly lists of new books, with some reviews.
302. **Science News Letter.** Lists scientific books of the week.
303. **Scientific Monthly.** Lists and some reviews.
304. **The Scientist.** Lists and excellent reviews.
305. **Soil Science.** Excellent reviews.
306. **Stain Technology.** Reviews the literature in this field; excellent coverage.
307. **Stechert-Hafner Book News.** Excellent source, particularly of foreign publications.
308. **Tropical Diseases Bulletin.**
309. **Zeitschrift für Naturforschung;** ...
310. **Zeitschrift für Vitamin-, Hormon- und Fermentforschung.**
311. **Zhurnal Mikrobiologii, Epidemiologii I Immunobiologii.**

In addition see Abstracts—Bacteriology; most of the abstract sources at least list the books.

15

BOOKS—SELECTED LIST OF SOURCES

321. **ASLIB Book List.** British Assoc. Special Libraries and Information Bureaux. Clarke, London, and Hafner Publishing Co., New York. Books published in English language

only. British Scientific and Technical Books. 1935–
1952. 1956. London. Nearly 10,000 entries.

322. Biblio. Bulletin Bibliographique des Ouvrages parus en
langue française dans le monde entier. Librairie
Hachette, Paris.

323. Bibliographie der deutschen Bibliothek. Frankfurt,
Germany.

324. Bibliographie des Livres Français d'Industrie et de Technologie. 1930. J. B. Baillière et fils, Paris. Supple-
ments have been issued.

325. British Museum (Nat. Hist.) Library. 1903–1940. Catalogue
of the books, manuscripts, maps, and drawings in the
British Museum (Natural History), London. One of the
world's finest collections on natural history.

326. The British National Bibliography. 1950–date. Council of
British Nat. Bibliography, Ltd., British Museum, London.

327. Catalog of British Scientific and Technical Books. 1933.
British Science Guild, London.

328. The Cumulative Book Index. A world's list of books in the
English language. 1928–1932–date. H. W. Wilson Co.,
New York.

329. Deutsche Nationalbibliographie. Leipzig, Germany.

330. Foreign Scientific and Technical Books. Reproduced by
license of the U. S. Office of Alien Property Custodian.
J. W. Edwards, Publisher, and Edwards Bros., Inc., Ann
Arbor, Mich. About 500 titles of standard works, most of
them in German, have been made available by reprinting.

331. Guida Bibliografica Internazionale per il Chimico. 1952.
Libri e Riviste, Sanson, Edizion; Scientifiche, Milan.
Excellent listing, pp. 188–195.

332. Hawkins, R. R. (ed.). 1953. Scientific, medical and technical books published in the United States of America.
2d supplement. Washington, D. C. A list of over 10,000
books with annotations. 579 pp.

333. Jackson, L. (ed.). 1951. Technical libraries. Their organization and management. Special Libraries Assoc.,
New York. Section, "Books and miscellaneous publications, selection and acquisition," is a very valuable section, pp. 39–55. This includes source lists for general
science as well as specific areas. Selections of newly
published books. Publishers of scientific books. Dealers in new books. Dealers in out-of-print books. Translations, etc.

334. Lewis' medical, scientific, and technical lending library catalog. 1950. H. K. Lewis & Co., London. This contains about 27,000 titles. Supplement, 1953. Bimonthly lists.

335. The Library of Congress Catalog. 1942. A cumulative list of works represented by Library of Congress Printed Cards. Library of Congress, Washington, D. C. Supplement, 1950, Subject catalog. Army Medical Library Catalog.

336. List of German Books on Chemical and Cognate Subjects. Published 1939–1946. 1946. H. McCombie & A. E. Cummins. Chemical Council. London.

337. New Books List. Denver Public Library, Science and Engineering Department.

338. New Technical Books. New York Public Library, Science and Technology Division.

339. Publishers Trade List Annual. R. R. Bowker Co., New York.

340. Publishers Weekly. Since 1950 cumulative lists of science-technology titles have been issued. This includes a list of books and pamphlets published each week in the United States.

341. Reference Catalogue of Current Literature. 1957. 2 vols. London. A list of all the books in print in the United Kingdom up to 1957.

342. Science Library; Bibliographical Series (No. 275). 1936. Select list of books on bacteriology and its industrial applications, exclusive of medicine, 1930–date.

343. Subject Guide to Books in Print. 1957. An index to the publisher's trade list annual. Ed. by Anstaett, H. B., and Prakken, S. L. R. R. Bowker Co., New York. Ninety-one thousand titles.

344. The United States Quarterly Book Review.

345. The United States Catalog. Books in Print, January 1, 1912–1928. H. W. Wilson & Co., New York.

346. Thornton, J. L., and Tully, R. I. J. 1954. Scientific books, libraries, and collectors. A study of bibliography and the book trade in relation to science. The Library Association, London. 288 pp. Bibliography, pp. 243–269.

347. Winchell, C. M. 1951. Guide to reference books. 7th ed. American Library Assoc., Chicago. 645 pp. Supplement, Winchell, C. M., and Johnson, O. A. 1954. 117 pp. Supplement, 1956. Winchell, C. M.

In addition, note the following selective list of American publications in bacteriology of great historical importance:

348. **McClung, L. S.** 1944. Early American publications relating to bacteriology. I. Textbooks, monographs, addresses, etc. Bact. Revs., 8, 119–160. An excellent American historical collection. This covers the field of American publications up to 1915. Since 1930 they are listed in "Scientific, medical, and technical books published in the United States of America." (See Hawkins, R. R.). Dr. Robert A. Greene, Los Angeles, Calif., has a list of American Publications in Bacteriology, 1915–1930.

16

CATALOGS

358. **International Catalog of Scientific Literature.** Issued in 17 parts, of which Section R. Bacteriology; 14 vols. (1902–1920); published for the International Council by The Royal Society of London, 1902–1919. The financial burden became so great that activities ceased after publication of the 1914 volumes. Has author and subject indexes, but difficult to use. Title entries. Very comprehensive for the earlier literature.

359. **Ramsay, A.** 1900, 1905, 1913. The scientific roll ... bacteria. Published as a periodical; incomplete and no more published. Over 2,000 entries.

360. **The Review of Bacteriology.** 1911–1919. Afterward: Protozoology and general parasitology; an epitome of general parasitology, bacteriology, and allied subjects in their relationship to pathology and hygiene. Ed. by Foulerton, A. G. R., and Slater, C. No more published. Over 3,000 entries.

361. **Underwood, E. A.** 1950. Catalogue of an exhibition illustrating medicine in 1850. Publications of the Wellcome Historical Medical Museum, Occasional Papers Series, No. 2. Oxford Univ. Press. 64 pp. Catalog divided into 15 sections; No. 6, Microscopic technique and histology. No. 7, Pathology and bacteriology. No. 13, Infectious disease. No. 14, Public health.

17

CONGRESSES

371. **Congrès International de Microscopie Electronique.**
     1. Paris, 1950.
     2. Paris, 1953.
     3. London, 1954.
372. **Congrès International de Microbiologie.**
     1. Paris, 1930.
     2. London, 1936.
     3. New York, 1939.
     4. Copenhagen, 1947.
     5. Rio de Janeiro, 1950.
     6. Rome, 1953.

     Abstracts of papers. Every three years. Text in English,
     French, or Portuguese.

18

DICTIONARIES

382. **Ainsworth, G. C., and Bisby, G. R. A.** 1954. A dictionary
     of the fungi. 4th ed. Commonwealth Mycological Insti-
     tute, Kew (Surrey). 475 pp. Lists alphabetically the
     generic names of fungi used through 1948. Heavy on
     medical mycology. Bibliography. Brief biographies of
     authorities.
383. **Bibliography of Interlingual Scientific and Technical Dic-
     tionaries.** 1953. UNESCO. Printed in France. Only one
     reference to microbiology, p. 57. Useful for wider cover-
     age, such as biology, botany, etc.
384. **Biraud, Y.** 1944. Polyglot dictionary of communicable
     diseases. *In* League of Nations Health Organization
     Bulletin, 10, 202–556.
385. **Hauduroy, P.** *et al.* 1953. Dictionnaire des bactéries
     pathogènes pour l'homme, les animaux et les plantes;
     suivi de la liste des êtres microscopiques conserves
     dans les collections de cultures types. 2d ed. Masson
     et Cie, Paris. 692 + 64 pp. Bacteria are listed alpha-

betically, with synonyms. Brief descriptions, properties,
and references. Useful for taxonomy and especially
pathogenic bacteria.

386. **Jacobs, M. B., Gerstein, M. J., and Walter, W. G.** 1955.
Dictionary of microbiology. D. Van Nostrand Co., Inc.,
Princeton, N. J. 300 pp. Variety of information on
organisms.

387. **Karel, L., and Roach, E. S.** 1951. A dictionary of antibiosis. Columbia Univ. Press. 373 pp. Lists antibiotics,
names of organisms inhibited, and those not affected.
Excellent bibliography.

388. **Partridge, W.** 1927. Dictionary of bacteriological equiva-
lents; French-English, German-English, Italian-English,
Spanish-English. Williams & Wilkins Co., Baltimore.
Useful for medical bacteriology.

19

DOCTORAL DISSERTATIONS

See:

398. **Winchell, C. M.** 1951. Guide to reference books. 7th ed.
Amer. Library Assoc., Library of Congress, Washington
D. C. Section G. Dissertations. Bibliography International, pp. 111–115. Also, Supplement, Winchell, C. M.,
and Johnson, O. A. 1954. P. 20. General lists and by
countries, e.g., Austria, Belgium, Canada, France,
Germany, Great Britain, Netherlands, Scandinavia, Spain,
South Africa, Switzerland, United States. Supplement.
1956. Winchell, C. M.

20

ENCYCLOPEDIAS AND MANUALS

This is a selective list with reference to emphasis on
history.

408. **Breed, R. S., Murray, E. G. D., and Hitchems, A. P. (et al.)**
1948. Bergey's manual of determinative bacteriology.

6th ed. Williams & Wilkins Co., Baltimore. 1529 pp.
Tabulated descriptions of 1,630 species of bacteria. Excellent bibliographic citations. Tremendous historical
development. (7th ed., 1957.)

409. **Buchanan, R. E.,** and **Fulmer, E. I.** 1928–1930. Physiology
and biochemistry of bacteria. 3 vols. Williams &
Wilkins Co., Baltimore. Exhaustive survey. Excellent
bibliographies.

410. **Doerr, R.,** and **Hallauer, C.** (eds.). 1938–1939. 2 vols.
Supplement, 1944. Second supplement, 1950. Hand-
buch der Virusforschung. Springer, Wien. Very comprehensive. Contributions by experts from various
countries.

411. **Duclaux, E.** 1898. Traité de Microbiologie. Masson et
Cie, Paris. 4 vols. One of the great early classics.

412. **Gay, F. P.** *et al.* 1935. Agents of disease and host resistance. C. C Thomas, Springfield, Ill. 1581 pp. Excellent short chapter on "The historical development of
our concepts of the nature and causation of disease,"
pp. 3–11, and "The history of bacteriology, particularly in
its relation to disease," pp. 120–147. Also excellent
list of references of historical importance following each
chapter.

413. **Great Britain's Medical Research Council.** 1929–1931. 9
vols. A system of bacteriology in relation to medicine.
H. M. S. O., London. Comprehensive work; excellent
history of medical bacteriology. Not as detailed as Kolle
and Wassermann.

414. **Kolle, W.,** and **Wassermann, A. von.** (eds.). 1927–1931.
Handbuck der pathogenen Mikroorganismen 3 Aufl. mit
Einschluss der Immunitätslehre und Epidemologie sowie
der Mikrobiologischen Diagnostik und Technik. Bearb.
und hrsg. von Kolle, W., Kraus, R. (*et al.*). G. Fischer,
Jena. 10 vols. and index (in vol. 19). This with the
Great Britain's Medical Research Council are the great
sources for bacteriologists for the earlier period of
bacteriology. Both are authoritative and comprehensive.
(Neither work has been revised.)

415. **Levaditi, C.,** and **Lépine, P.** (*et al.*) 1948. Les ultravirus
des maladies humaines. 2d ed. Maloine, Paris. 2 vols.
1180 pp. Good review and bibliography.

416. **Van Rooyen, C. E., and Rhodes, A. J.** 1948. Virus diseases of man. 2d ed. Thomas Nelson & Sons, New York.
1202 pp. Reference work of top importance on medical
virology.
417. **Wilson, G. S., and Miles, A. A.** 1955. Topley and Wilson's
principles of bacteriology and immunity. 4th ed. Williams
& Wilkins Co., Baltimore. 2 vols. 2331 pp. Extensive
treatment of medical bacteriology. Excellent list of
references and index.

21

HANDBOOKS AND TABLES

427. **Handbook of Biological Data.** 1956. National Academy of
Sciences. National Research Council, Washington, D. C.
428. **Jackson, L.** (ed.). 1951. Technical libraries. Special
Libraries Assoc., New York. Listings of engineering
handbooks, chemical, and physical data, handbooks,
technical dictionaries, and encyclopedias, etc., pp. 158-
161. In addition, see section on pharmacy, p. 187.

22

IMMUNOLOGY

ABSTRACTS

438. **Biological Abstracts.** 1926–date. Union of American Biological Societies, Univ. of Pennsylvania. Section C; includes immunology.
439. **Bulletin de l'Institut Pasteur.** 1903–date. Paris.
440. **Ergebnisse der Hygiene, Bakteriologie, Immunitätsforschung
und Experimentellen Pharmakologie.** 1914–date. Berlin.
441. **Excerpta Medica.** 1947–date. Amsterdam, The Netherlands.
442. **Index Medicus.** 1879–date. Now, Quarterly cumulative index medicus. Chicago.

443. Jahresbericht über die Ergebnisse der Immunitätsforschung. 1905-1912. Stuttgart, Germany. Superseded by Ergebnisse der Hygiene, Bakteriologie, Immunitätsforschung und Experimentellen Pharmakologie.
444. Japanese Journal of Medical Sciences. 1929–date. Tokyo.
445. Zentralblatt für die gesamte Hygiene mit Einschluss der Bakteriologie und Immunitätslehre. 1922–date. Berlin.
446. Zhurnal Mikrobiologii, Epidemiologii I Immunobiologii. 1924–date. Moscow. Also original research, analyses, book reviews, news notes, bibliographies.

ANALYSES AND ORIGINAL RESEARCH

447. Acta Serologica et Immunologica. 1940–date. Tokyo.
448. Antonie van Leeuwenhoek; Journal of Microbiology and Serology. 1934–date. Amsterdam, Netherlands. Also original research.
449. Arbeiten aus dem Paul-Ehrlich-Institut, dem Georg-Speyer-Haus und dem Ferdinand-Bluhm-Institut zu Frankfurt am Main. 1906–irregular. Also original research.
450. Arbeiten aus dem Sero-Bakteriologischen Institut der Universität Helsinki. 1928–date. Helsinki, Finland. Also original research.
451. Blood Group News; Anthropological, Biochemical, Clinical, Forensic, Genetical, Serological. 1949–date. Copenhagen, Denmark. Bibliographies.
452. Bollettino dell'Instituto Sieroterapico Milanese: Archivio di Microbiologia ed Immunologia. 1917–date. Milan, Italy.
453. Communications de Statens Seruminstitut; Extraits. 1906–irregular. Copenhagen, Denmark.
454. Ergebnisse der Hygiene, Bakteriologie, Immunitätsforschung und Experimentellen Therapie. 1914–irregular. Berlin.
455. Immunology. 1958–date. London. The official journal of the British Society for Immunology.
456. Journal of Immunology. 1916–date. Baltimore, Md. Mainly original research.
457. Meddelelser Fra Statens Veterinaere Serumlaboratorium. 1932–irregular. Copenhagen, Denmark. Also original research.
458. Medicine and Biology. 1942–date. Tokyo. Also original research.

459. Notiziario dell'Instituto Vaccinogeno Antitubercolare. 1951–date. Milan, Italy. Mainly original research.
460. Revue d'Immunologie. 1935–date. Paris.
461. Revue Française de Sérologie et Chimiothérapie; Nouvelle Série. 1951–date. Paris. Also proceedings of societies, news notes.
462. Schmidt, H. 1950. Fortschritte der Serologie. Frankfurt-am-Main. To be completed in 14 Lieferungen. Reviews with bibliographies.
463. The Serological Museum; Bulletin. 1948?–irregular. New Brunswick, N. J.
464. Trudy Leningradskogo Instituta Vaktsin I Syvorotok. 1944–date. Leningrad. Vaccines and serums.
465. Voprosy Vozrastnoi Immunologii. 1947–date. Leningrad.

Also, see Journals—Original Research; Analyses.

23

JOURNALS—ORIGINAL RESEARCH*

475. *Acta Microbiologica. 1954–date. Budapest, Hungary. Text in English, French, German, or Russian.
476. Acta Pathologica et Microbiologica Scandinavica. 1924–date. Copenhagen, Denmark. Text in English, French, German, or Russian; summaries in English. Eight times a year.
477. Acta Pathologica et Microbiologica Scandinavica; Supplementum. 1923–irregular. Copenhagen, Denmark. Text in English, French, or German; summaries in various languages.
478. Acta Physiologica Academiae Scientiarum Hungaricae. 1950–irregular. Budapest, Hungary. Text in English, French, German, or Russian; summaries in various languages.

*Based on listings from Biological Sciences Serial Publications. A World List, 1950–1954. 1955. Biological Abstracts, Philadelphia.

479. *Acta Virologica. 1957–date. Prague. Quarterly, in English.
480. *Anais de Microbiologia. 1951–date. Rio de Janeiro, Brazil.
481. Annales de l'Institut Pasteur. 1887–date. Paris. Text in English or French; includes "Séances de la Société Française de Microbiologie."
482. Annales de l'Institut Pasteur de Lille. 1948–date. Paris.
483. Antonie van Leeuwenhoek; Journal of Microbiology and Serology. 1934–date. Amsterdam, Netherlands. Text in English, French, or German. Four times a year.
484. Applied Microbiology. 1953–date. Baltimore, Md.
485. Arbeiten aus dem Sero-Bakteriologischen Institut der Universität Helsinki. 1929–date. Helsinki, Finland. Text in English or German; occasional summaries in other languages.
486. Archiv für Hygiene und Bakteriologie; Forschungsarbeiten aus Hygiene und Mikrobiologie Einschliesslich Öffentlicher Gesundheitspflege, Gewerbehygiene und Sozialhygiene. 1883–irregular. Munich, Germany. Summaries in English, French, and German.
487. Archiv für Mikrobiologie; Zeitschrift für die Erforschung des Pflanzlichen Mikroorganismen. 1930–irregular. Berlin. Occasional articles in English.
488. Archives d'Anatomie Microscopique et de Morphologie Experimentale. 1897–date. Paris. Quarterly.
489. Archives de l'Institut Pasteur d'Algérie. 1923–date. Algiers. Quarterly.
490. Archives de l'Institut Pasteur de la Guyane. 1951–date. Cahors, France. Includes the Institute's "Publications" and "Rapport sur le Fonctionnement Technique."
491. Archives de l'Institut Pasteur du Maroc. 1932–irregular. Casablanca, French Morocco.
492. Arquivos do Instituto Bacteriológico Câmara Pestana. 1906–irregular. Text in French or Portuguese; summaries in English.
493. Bacteriological Reviews. 1937–date. Baltimore, Md. Quarterly. Mainly a review journal.
494. *Boletín Instituto Bacteriologico de Chile. 1942–date. Santiago, Chile.
495. Bollettino dell'Instituto Sieroterapico Milanese; Archivio di Microbiologia ed Immunologia. 1917–date. Milan,

Italy. Text in Italian; summaries in English and Italian. Bimonthly.

496. Canadian Journal of Microbiology. 1954–date. Ottawa, Canada. Bimonthly.

497. *Communications du Laboratoire Bactériologique de l'État Suédois; Meddelanden Från Statens Bakteriologiske Laboratorium. Date? Stockholm, Sweden. Text in English, French, or Swedish; Swedish papers have occasional summaries in other languages.

498. Ergebnisse der Hygiene, Bakteriologie, Immunitätsforschung und Experimentellen Therapie. 1914–irregular. Berlin.

499. Giornale di Batteriologia e Immunologia. 1926–date. Turin, Italy.

500. Japanese Journal of Bacteriology. 1944–date. Tokyo. Text in Japanese. Bimonthly.

501. The Journal of Applied Bacteriology. 1945–irregular. Reading, England.

502. Journal of Applied Mycology. 1946–irregular. Sapporo, Japan. Text in Japanese, with occasional summaries in English.

503. Journal of Bacteriology. 1916–date. Baltimore, Md.

504. The Journal of Dairy Research. 1929–date. London.

505. The Journal of General Microbiology. 1947–irregular. London.

506. Journal of Hygiene, Epidemiology, Microbiology and Immunology. 1957–date. Prague. Articles are in English, French, or German. Quarterly.

507. The Journal of Pathology and Bacteriology. 1892–date. London. Quarterly.

508. *The Laboratory Journal. 1913–irregular. London.

509. Lobund Reports. 1946–irregular. Notre Dame, Ind.

510. Meddelelser Fra Hygienisk-Bakteriologiske Laboratorium den Kgl. Veterinaer- og Landbohøjskole. 1947?–irregular. Copenhagen, Denmark. Text in Danish or English.

511. Medycyna Doswiadczalna I Mikrobiologia. 1949–date. Warsaw, Poland. Quarterly.

512. Microbiología Española. 1947–date. Madrid, Spain. Quarterly.

513. Microentomology. 1936–irregular. Stanford, Calif.

514. *Mikrobiologcheskii Sbornik. Date? Erevan, USSR. Text in Armenian and Russian.

515. **Mikrobiologichnyi Zhurnal.** 1934–date. Kiev, USSR. Quarterly.
516. **Mikrobiologiia.** 1932–date. Moscow.
517. **Mikrokosmos; Zeitschrift für Angewandte Mikroskopie, Mikrobiologie, Mikrochemie und Mikroskropische Technik.** 1907–date. Stuttgart, Germany.
518. **Milchwissenschaftliche Berichte.** 1951–irregular. Wolfpassing, Austria.
519. **Milchwissenschaft; Internationale Forschungsberichte und Nachrichten aus der Gesamten Milchwirtschaft für Wissenschaft und Praxis.** 1946–date. Nuremberg, Germany. Occasional articles in English; summaries in English, French, German, and Spanish.
520. **Publications, Institut Pasteur de la Guyane.** 1940–irregular. Cahors, France. A subseries of the Institute's "Archives," beginning January, 1951. Monographic series.
521. ***Report, Virus Research Institute.** Date? Entebba, Uganda.
522. **Revista del Instituto Bacteriológico "Dr. Carlos G. Malbran."** 1917–irregular. Buenos Aires, Argentina.
523. **Schweizerische Zeitschrift für Allgemeine Pathologie und Bakteriologie;** Revue Suisse de Pathologie Générale et de Bacteriologie; Swiss Journal of General Pathology and Bacteriology. 1938–date. Basel, Switzerland. Text in French, German, and Italian. Bimonthly.
524. **Schweizerische Zeitschrift für Allgemeine Pathologie und Bakteriologie; Supplementum.** 1942?–irregular. Basel, Switzerland.
525. **Symposia of the Section on Microbiology, New York Academy of Medicine.** Date?–irregular. New York.
526. **Travaux du Laboratoire de Microbiologie de la Faculté de Pharmacie de Nancy.** 1928–date. Nancy, France.
527. **Trudove na Mikrobiologicheskiia Institut.** 1950–irregular. Sofia, Bulgaria. Text in Bulgarian, summaries in French. Monographic series.
528. ***Trudy Instituta Mikrobiologii.** 1951–? Moscow.
529. **Trudy Vsesoiuznogo Nauchno-Issledovatel'skogo Instituta Sel'Skokhoziastvennoi Mikrobiologii.** 1949–date. Moscow.
530. **Turkish Bulletin of Hygiene and Experimental Biology;** Türk Ijiyen ve Tecrübî Biyoloji Dergisi. 1941–irregular. Text in English, German, or Turkish; Turkish papers have summaries in English.

531. Virology. 1955–date. Academic Press, Inc., New York.
532. Virus; Journal of Virology. 1951–date. Kyoto, Japan.
533. *Wei Sheng Wu Hsüeh Pao. Date? Peking, China.
534. Zeitschrift für Immunitätsforschung und Experimentelle
     Therapie. 1908–date. Stuttgart, Germany. Quarterly.
535. Zeitschrift für Zellforschung und Mikroskopische Anatomie.
     1924–irregular. Berlin.
536. Zentralblatt für Bakteriologie, Parasitenkunde, Infektions-
     krankheiten und Hygiene; 1. Abteilung: Medizinische-
     Hygienische Bakteriologie, Virusforschung und
     Parasitologie; Originale. 1887–irregular.
537. Zentralblatt für Bakteriologie, Parasitenkunde, Infektions-
     krankheiten und Hygiene; 2. Abteilung: Allgemeine,
     Landwirtschaftliche, Technische, Nahrungsmittel-
     Bakteriologie und Mykologie, Protozoologie, Pflanzen-
     krankheiten ... 1895–irregular.
538. Zhurnal Mikrobiologii, Epidemiologii I Immunobiologii.
     1924–date. Moscow.

24

LABORATORIES—UNITED STATES

548. Directory of Biological Laboratories. 1950. 4th ed. Burns
     Comp. and Research Org., Chicago. Comprehensive list
     of laboratories in the United States and Canada con-
     cerned with biochemical, bacteriological, or biological
     investigations.
549. Directory of Hydrobiological Laboratories and Personnel in
     North America. 1954. Hiatt, R. W. (ed.). Univ. of
     Hawaii Press, Honolulu.
550. Jack, H. A. 1945. Biological field stations of the world.
     Chronica Botanica Series III, vol. 9. The Ronald Press
     Co., New York. International.
551. National Research Council: Industrial Research Labora-
     tories of the United States. 1955. 10th ed. The Council,
     Washington, D. C. 444 pp. Useful for locating industrial
     laboratories concerned with biology, bacteriology, etc.
     Includes consulting research laboratories.

552. Physicians Desk Reference to Pharmaceutical Specialties and Biologicals. 1954. 8th ed. Medical Economics, Inc., Rutherford, N. J.
553. Society of American Bacteriologists. 1954. Directory and constitution.
554. U. S. National Bureau of Standards. 1946. Directory of commercial and college laboratories. Government Printing Office, Washington, D. C.

Also:

555. Koenig, E. 1957. A directory of medical and biological research institutes of the U.S.S.R. Preliminary edition, National Institutes of Health, Washington, D. C. 38 pp.

25

LECTURES

565. The Harvey Lectures. 1905–date. Latest series published by Academic Press, Inc., New York. Latest findings in selected phases of anatomy, physiology, zoology, *bacteriology*, physiological and pathological chemistry.

26

LITERATURE—GENERAL GUIDE

575. Bulloch, W. 1938. The history of bacteriology. Oxford Univ. Press. See section, "Biographical notices of some of the early workers in bacteriology," pp. 349–406, for excellent information on the publications of these famous early bacteriologists.
576. Doe, J., and Marshall, M. L. (eds.). 1956. Medical library practice. 2d ed. American Library Assoc., Chicago. 601 pp. Excellent source for medical bacteriology.

577. **Fleming, T. P.** 1952. Guide to the literature of science. Columbia University, School of Library Service, New York. 46 pp. Mimeographed. Not comprehensive enough for bacteriology.

578. **Flügge, C. G. F. W.** 1883. Fermente und Mikroparasiten. F. C. W. Vogel, Leipzig. 2d ed. Transl. by Cheyne, W., under the title, "Microorganisms with special reference to the etiology of the infective diseases," by the Sydenham Soc., 1890. This devotes 63 pages to the literature.

579. **Index-Catalogue of the Library of the Surgeon General's Office.** United States Army. Second Series, vol. II. 1897. "History of bacteriology," pp. 38–39. Third Series, vol. II. 1920. Government Printing Office, Washington D. C. List of articles on the "History of bacteriology," p. 303, and listing historical publications in "Bacteriology in relation to medicine," pp. 310–311. Fourth Series, vol. II. 1937. History of bacteriology, p. 43. Fourth Series, vol. XI. 1955. History of Microbiology, pp. 20–21.

580. **Jenkins, F. B.** 1954. University of Illinois. Library school, science reference sources; a selected list of titles for use in Library Science 412. Illini Union Bookstore, Champaign, Ill. Includes section for microbiology.

581. **Magnin, A.** 1880. The bacteria. Transl. by Sternberg, G. M. Little, Brown, & Co. Boston. 227 pp. This contains a rather complete bibliography up to that time. See pp. 191–222.

Also:

582. **Morton, L. T.** 1954. Garrison and Morton's medical bibliography. An annotated check-list of texts illustrating the history of medicine. 2d ed. Printed by W. J. Rawlinson, Ltd., Netherlands. See section, bacteriology, pp. 215–221; section, infection; immunology; serology, pp. 221–225; section, allergy and anaphylaxis, pp. 226–228. This is an excellent list for the medical bacteriologist. There are also other related sections worthy of perusal.

583. **Oatfield, H.** 1950. Literature of the chemical periphery, II. Bacteriology. Bull. Med. Library Assoc., 38, 156–165. This is one of the best contemporary listings for bacteriologists that has been published.

584. **Smith, E. F.** 1905. Bacteria in relation to plant diseases. Carnegie Institution of Washington, Washington D. C. An

extensive annotated bibliography of the early publications
in bacteriology, pp. 203–266.

585. **Sternberg, G. M.** 1892. A manual of bacteriology. W. Wood
& Co., New York. 886 pp. Extensive coverage of earlier
literature.

586. **Winchell, C. M.** 1951. Guide to reference books. 7th ed.
American Library Assoc., Chicago. 645 pp. Supplement,
1954, 117 pp. Supplement, 1956. Note excellent listings
of bibliographies, periodicals, special section on bacteriology, etc.

Also see Catalogs, etc.

27

PERIODICALS—SOURCES FOR

596. **British Union—Catalogue of Periodicals.** A record of the
periodicals of the world, from the 17th century to the
present day, in British libraries. Academic Press, Inc.,
New York, and Butterworth's Scientific Publications,
London. Vol. 1, A–C, 1955; vol. 2, D–K, 1956.

597. **The Union List of Serials in Libraries of the United States
and Canada.** 1943. 2d ed. Ed. by Gregory, W., and an
Advisory Committee appointed by the American Library
Assoc., New York. H. W. Wilson Co., New York. 3,052
pp. This is a monumental work, the most important of its
kind. Over 650 libraries have cooperated in preparing the
almost 120,000 titles, of every kind, dead or alive, published in about 70 languages.

598. **A World List of Scientific Periodicals Published in the
Years 1900–1950.** 1952. 3d ed. by Smith, W. A., Kent,
F. L., and Stratton, G. B. Butterworth's Scientific Publications, London. 1,058 pp. Lists over 50,000 titles
showing location in 247 British libraries. Not as useful
as Union List.

599. **World Medical Periodicals—Les Périodiques médicaux dans
le Monde—Periódicos Médicos del Mundo—Medizinische
Zeitschriften aller Länder.** 1957. 2d ed. New York.

In addition see:

600. **Crane, E. J., Patterson, A. M., and Marr, E. B.** 1957. A guide to the literature of chemistry. John Wiley & Sons, Inc., New York. Pp. 64–157. Also, bibliography of lists of periodicals, pp. 357–359.

601. **Doe, J., and Marshall, M. L.** (eds.). 1956. Medical library practice. 2d ed. American Library Assoc., Chicago. List of periodicals, pp. 351–352.

602. **Winchell, C. M.** 1951. Guide to reference books. 7th ed. American Library Assoc., Chicago. Pp. 255–256. Supplement, 1954. Winchell, C. M., and Johnson, O. A., pp. 48–49. Supplement, 1956. Winchell, C. M. In addition add: Bibliography of Scientific Publications of South and South East Asia. 1955. Vol. 1. UNESCO. Science Cooperation Offices for South and South East Asia. INSDOC, National Physical Laboratory, New Delhi, India. 1957. 188 pp.

603. **WHO-UNESCO.** 1953. World medical periodicals. UNESCO & WHO, Columbia Univ. Press. More than 4,000 entries.

Also note excellent listings in:

604. **Biological Sciences Serial Publications.** A World List, 1950–1954. 1955. Biological Abstracts, Philadelphia. See listings such as: Antibiotics, pp. 44–45; Bacteriology, pp. 65–67; Biochemistry and biophysics, pp. 41–44; Enzymology, p. 45; History of science, pp. 192–193; Microbiology, pp. 62–65; Microscopy, pp. 76–77; Mycology, pp. 97–98; Serology, pp. 67–68; Virology, p. 68.

28

PROCEEDINGS

614. **Abstracts of Papers.** International Congress for Microbiology. 1930-every 3 years. International Association of Microbiologists. Also abstracts. Text in English, French, or Portuguese.

615. Acta Pathologica et Microbiologica Scandinavica; Supplementum. 1923-irregular. Copenhagen, Denmark. Monographic series, also includes original research. Text in English, French, or German; summaries in various languages.

616. Acta Physiologica Academiae Scientiarum Hungaricae. 1950-irregular. Also original research and analyses. Text in English, French, German, or Russian; summaries in various languages.

617. Annales de l'Institut Pasteur. 1887-date. Paris. Also original research and analyses. Text in English or French.

618. Bacteriological Proceedings. 1901-date. Baltimore, Md.

619. Bulletin de l'Association des Diplomés de Microbiologie de la Faculté de Pharmacie de Nancy. 1931-date. Nancy, France.

620. The Journal of Applied Bacteriology. 1945-irregular. Reading, England. Also original research and analyses.

621. The Journal of General Microbiology. 1947-irregular. Cambridge, London. Also original research.

622. The Journal of Pathology and Bacteriology. 1892-date. London. Also original research, analyses, and book reviews.

623. Mikrobiologji Dergisi; Revu de Microbiologie. 1948-date. Istanbul, Turkey. Text in Turkish; summaries in English or French.

624. Revue Française de Sérologie et Chimothérapie; Nouvelle Serie. 1951-date. Paris. Also news notes.

625. Schweizerische Zeitschrift für Allgemeine Pathologie und Bakteriologie; Revue Suisse de Pathologie Générale et de Bacteriologie; Swiss Journal of General Pathology and Bacteriology. 1938-date. Basel, Switzerland. Text in French or German; summaries in English, French, German, and Italian. Also original research, analyses, and book reviews.

29

RUSSIAN LITERATURE

635. Abstracts of Soviet Medicine. 1957. Part A (Basic Medical Sciences) includes a section on medical microbiology,

immunology, and serology. Translation. Excerpta Medica
Foundation.

636. Babsky, E. B., Kochergin, I. G., and Parin, V. V. 1945.
Microbiology and epidemiology: Being a volume in the
series, "Achievements of Soviet Medicine in the Patriotic
War." Transl. by Fox, H. P. Medical Publishers, London.
158 pp.

637. Bibliography of Translations from Russian Scientific and
Technical Literature. Card Division of the Library of
Congress. A recently established pool of translations
from Russian scientific and technical literature housed at
the Library of Congress under the sponsorship of the
National Science Foundation and the Atomic Energy
Commission.

638. Grabar, P. 1956. Review of the microbiological and immunological literature published in 1955 in the U.S.S.R.
Ann. Rev. Microbiol., 10, 51–84. More of a catalog
than a review. 195 references. Indicates principal Russian journals. 1957. Ann. Rev. Microbiol., 11, 43–76.
192 references.

639. Guide to Russian Scientific Periodical Literature. 1948–
1951. Directed by Turkevich, J., and Turkevich, Ludmila.
Princeton University. Information and Publications Division, Brookhaven National Laboratory, Upton, N. Y.
"The purpose of this publication is to make available to
scientists in this country, most of whom are unfamiliar
with the Russian language, the contents of the Russian
scientific periodical literature."

640. Isachenko, B. L. 1942. (Microbiology in the U.S.S.R. for
25 years, 1917–1942). Mikrobiologia, Moskva, 11, No. 5,
pp. i–xvi.

641. ———. 1946. Excerpts from history of microbiology in
Russia. Amer. Rev. Soviet Med., 3, 549–566.

642. The Monthly List of Russian Accessions. 1948-date.
Library of Congress, Superintendent of Documents, U. S.
Government Printing Office, Washington, D. C.

643. Scientific and Technical Serial Publications; Soviet Union
1945–1953. 1954. Monograph. Superintendent of Documents, U. S. Government Printing Office, Washington,
D. C.

644. Uspensky, E. E. 1937. (Main principles and achievements
of Soviet microbiology during the last 20 years.) Mikrobiologia, Moskva, 6, 948–963.

645. **Waksman, S. A.** 1946–1947. Microbiology in the Soviet
Union. Amer. Rev. Soviet Med., 4, 314–321.
646. _____. 1947. Microbiology in the U.S.S.R. in 1946.
Sc. Month., 64, 289–296.

In addition, a contemporary article of great interest:

647. **O'Dette, R. E.** 1957. Russian translation. Science, 125,
579–585. Contains 21 important references and notes.

Also note:

648. **Journal of Microbiology, Epidemiology, and Immunology.**
(Transl. from the Russian.) Bauer, D. J., scientific translation editor. Perganion Institute, New York. Monthly
from 1957.
649. **Scientific and Technical Translating.** And other aspects of
the language problem. 1957. United Nations Educational,
Scientific and Cultural Organization. Paris. 282 pp.

30

SOCIETY OF AMERICAN BACTERIOLOGISTS

659. **Clark, P. F.** 1953. A half century of Presidential addresses
of the Society of American Bacteriologists. Bact. Revs.,
17, 213–247.
660. **Cohen, B.** 1940. The history programs of the Society of
American Bacteriologists. Bull. Inst. Hist. Med., 8,
312–313.
661. _____. 1950. Chronicles of the Society of American
Bacteriologists. The Williams & Wilkins Co., Baltimore.
83 pp. Photographs of Presidents of the Society, 1900–
1950. General information about the society.
662. **Conn, H. J.** 1948. Professor Herbert William Conn and the
founding of the society (S.A.B.). Bact. Revs., 12, 275–
296.
663. **Harris, N. M.** 1926. Our society—in retrospect and pros-
pect. (S.A.B.). Jour. Bact., 11, 153–164.
664. **Harrison, F. C.** 1922. Our society (S.A.B.). Jour. Bact.,
7, 149–157.

665. Sedgwick, W. T. 1916. The genesis of a new science—
     bacteriology. Jour. Bact., 1, 1–4.
666. Thom, C. 1940. Out of the furrow. Jour. Bact., 41, 1–15.
667. Winslow, C.-E. A. 1940. The first forty years of the so-
     ciety of American bacteriologists. Science, 91, 125–129.

Also, see numerous address by Presidents of the Society
published in Bacteriological Reviews.

31

SOCIETIES

677. Bates, R. S. 1945. Scientific societies in the United
     States. John Wiley & Sons, Inc., New York. Biblio-
     ography, pp. 193–220. (2d ed., 1958. 308 pp.)
678. Buttress, F. A. 1945. World list of abbreviations of
     scientific, technological and commercial organizations.
     London. More than 2,500 abbreviations are listed, with
     the names of foreign organizations freely translated.
     Russian abbreviations are not included.
679. Directory of International Scientific Organizations. 1954.
     UNESCO. 2d ed. Paris. Distributed by Columbia Univ.
     Press.
680. National Research Council. 1948. Handbook of scientific
     and technical societies and institutions of the United
     States and Canada. 5th ed. National Research Council,
     Washington, D. C.
681. Winchell, C. M. 1951. Guide to reference books. 7th ed.
     Amer. Library Assoc. Library of Congress, Washington,
     D. C. Societies and Congresses, pp. 258–259. Sup-
     plement, 1954, p. 50. International listings. Supplement,
     1956, Winchell, C. M.

Part II

HISTORY OF BACTERIOLOGY—WITH SPECIAL REFERENCE TO SPECIFIC AREAS.

This section does not include biographies.

32

GENERAL HISTORY

691. **Bulloch, W.** 1930. The history of bacteriology. *In* A system of bacteriology. Medical Research Council, H.M. S.O., London. Vol 1, pp. 15-103. This is the classic which laid the foundation for Bulloch's book.

692. _____. 1938. The history of bacteriology. Oxford Univ. Press, London. 422 pp. This is the classic history of bacteriology. Unfortunately the title is incorrect; it should have been, The history of *medical* bacteriology. This is the most authoritative source that we have and any future history of bacteriology will be based on this tremendous foundation. The biographical index is, in itself, a remarkable feature. It is well worth while to read the review by Leikind, M. C. 1940. Isis, 31, 480-482. Leikind notes that Appert, N., is almost completely neglected. Pasteur's work on the economic aspects of bacteriology is only vaguely discussed. Furthermore, Robert Hooke was the first to confirm Leeuwenhoek's observation and not Joblot. Burrill, T. J., the pioneer American plant pathologist, was the first to prove a bacterium as the cause of a plant disease. Sewall, H., was the first to discover the phenomenon of antitoxic immunity. The book needs more on Jenner. Despite these minor points, this is the finest publication on the history of *medical* bacteriology ever written.

When the history of bacteriology is finally written, Bulloch's work on medical bacteriology will have to be expanded to take into consideration the wider scope and range of bacteriology.

693. **Ford, W. W.** 1939. Bacteriology. Paul B. Hoeber, Inc., New York. 207 pp. This is a brief history of medical

bacteriology but does not come up to the high standards set by Bulloch. Nevertheless, very valuable and has an excellent bibliography.

694. **Löffler, F.** 1887. Vorlesungen über die geschichtliche Entwickelung der Lehre von den Bacterien. Bis zum Jahre 1879. Erster Theil, F. C. W. Vogel, Leipzig. 252 pp. This is the first volume written on the history of bacteriology. In his preface, Löffler announced the plan of a second volume, but this was never completed. This volume, unfortunately, has many errors. The student should refer to the more accurate work of Bulloch.

There are numerous books, articles, and reviews covering certain areas of the history of bacteriology that may be found listed in:

695. **Index-Catalogue of the Library of the Surgeon General's Office.** United States Army (Army Medical Library) U. S. Government Printing Office, Washington, D. C., as well as in several abstract and index journals.

Also note listing in:

696. **Morton, L. T.** 1954. Garrison and Morton's medical bibliography. An annotated check-list of texts illustrating the history of medicine. 2d ed. Printed by W. J. Rawlinson, Ltd., Netherlands. See section, Bacteriology, pp. 215–225. Also excellent for other related fields. Arranged in chronological order. An annotated check list for the medical bacteriologist.

33

ACTINOMYCETES

706. **Waksman, S. A.** 1950. The Actinomycetes. Their nature, occurrence, activities, and importance. A Chronica Botanica Publication. The Ronald Press Co., New York. 230 pp. Extensive bibliography, pp. 199–221 (522 ref.). Waksman refers to the important early reviews found in

monographs such as: Lieske, R. (1921), Orskov, J. (1923), Duche, J. (1934), Kriss, A. E. (1937), and Krassilnikov, N. A. (1938 and 1941).

707. **Waksman, S. A.**, and **Lechevalier, H. A.** 1953. Guide to the classification and identification of the Actinomycetes and their antibiotics. The Williams & Wilkins Co., Baltimore. 246 pp. This is a handy guide to some of the important references. Selected general references, pp. 237–239 (58 ref.).

34

AIR

To the author's knowledge there is no single source devoted to the history of bacteriology of the air. The historian will have to refer to a number of different sources for information. Some of the following are possibly useful:

717. **Bulloch, W.** 1930. The history of bacteriology. *In* A system of bacteriology. Medical Research Council, H.M.S.O., London. Vol. 1, pp. 15–104.

718. _____. 1938. The history of bacteriology. Oxford Univ. Press, London. 422 pp.

719. **Duclaux, E.** 1898. Traité de microbiologie. Masson et Cie, Paris. Vol. 1, 632 pp. There are two excellent chapters, "Microbes de l'air," pp. 398–412, and "Distribution des germes dans l'air," pp. 413–424, that are of historical importance and refer to the publications of Duclaux (1891), Pasteur (1862), Miquel (1883), Petri (1887), Tyndall (1882), Buchner (1880 and 1888), and others.

720. **Ford, W. W.** 1939. Bacteriology. Paul B. Hoeber, Inc., New York. 207 pp.

721. **Wells, W. F.** 1955. Airborne contagion and air hygiene. An ecological study of droplet infections. Published for The Commonwealth Fund by Harvard Univ. Press. 423 pp. An extensive bibliography, pp. 379–404. Short historical references to Pasteur (1860), Petri (1887), Frankland

(1886), Committee on Standard Methods for the Examination of Air of the American Public Health Assoc. (1917), Controversies of Spallanzani (1765) and Needham (1776), Pouchet (1860 and 1864), Schwann (1837) and Schröder (1859) and Bastian (1901), Tyndall (1882), Pasteur (1860–1861), and others.

35

ANAEROBIC BACTERIA

GENERAL

731. Breed, R. S., Murray, E. G. D., and Hitchens, A. P. 1948. Bergey's manual of determinative bacteriology. 6th ed. Williams & Wilkins Co., Baltimore. Classification of anaerobic organisms with historical references. (7th ed., 1957.)

732. Bulloch, W. 1938. The history of bacteriology. Oxford Univ. Press, London. Note section "Anaerobiosis and the technical methods for anaerobic culture," pp. 232–234.

733. Hall, I. C. 1928. Anaerobiosis. In The newer knowledge of bacteriology and immunology. Ed. by Jordan, E. O., and Falk, I. S. Chicago Univ. Press. Pp. 198–210. An excellent historical discussion with listing of references. Starts with the important fundamental discoveries of Pasteur (1861, 1863, 1876, and 1877). Cites some important publications such as: (1) Jungano and Distaso. 1910. Les anaerobies. Masson, Paris; (2) Desderi, P. 1919. Infezione da germi anaerobi per ferità in guerra. Torino; (3) Fasiani, G. M. 1921 Bulletino dell'Instituto Sièroterapico Milanese, No. 3; (4) Lieske, R. 1921. Morphologie und Biologie der Strahlenpilze (Actinomyoetes). Leipzig; and other publications.

734. Hibler, E. von 1908. Untersuchungen über die pathogenen Anaeroben, über die anatomischen und histologischen Veränderungen bei den durch sie bedingten Infektionserkrankungen des Menschen sowie der Tiere und über

einige nichtpathogene Anaerobenarten. Gustav Fischer,
Jena. 415 pp. First general book published on this subject.

735. Weinberg, M., and Séguin, P. 1918. La Gangrène Gazeuse.
Masson et Cie, Paris. 335 pp. First monograph on this
subject.

SUBJECT BIBLIOGRAPHIES

745. Borowski, J. 1951. *In* Przglad Epidemiol., 7, 257–269. A
review of the Polish literature on anaerobic bacteria,
1945–1950. Cited by McClung, L. S. 1956. The anaerobic bacteria with special reference to the genus *Clostridium.* Ann. Rev. Microbiol., 10, 173 (Ref. No. 25).

746. Catalogue of Publications on Anaerobic Bacteria. 1954. In
the library of the Veterinary Inst., Veterinary Inst., Bogor,
Indonesia. 825 pp.

747. McClung, L. S., and McCoy, E. 1941. The anaerobic bacteria and their activities in nature and disease: A subject bibliography. Supplement one: Literature for 1935
and 1939. Univ. of California Press. 244 pp.

748. McCoy, E., and McClung, L. S. 1939. The anaerobic bacteria and their activities in nature and disease. A subject bibliography of the literature to 1937. 2 vols. Univ.
of California Press. Vol. 1, Author index. Vol. 2, Subject index. 295 pp. and 602 pp. Detailed subject bibliography excepting Slavic and oriental. Excellent for short
circuits around the abstract journals. 10,500 listings.

749. Spencer, M. C. 1953. Gas gangrene and gas gangrene
organisms: 1940–1952. An annotated bibliography of the
Russian literature, 1940–1952, and the non-Russian
literature for 1952. Reference Division, Armed Forces
Medical Library, Washington, D. C. 73 pp.

World War I occasioned the publication of the following
three special reports of some historical importance:

750. Committee upon Anaerobic Bacteria and Infections. Report
on the anaerobic infections of wounds and the bacteriological and serological problems arising therefrom. 1919.
Great Britain, Medical Research Council, Spec. Rpt. Ser.
No. 39. 182 pp. Both pathogenic and nonpathogenic
anaerobes.

751. Douglas, S. R., Fleming, A., and Colebrook, L. 1920.
     Studies in wound infections. Great Britain, Med. Res.
     Council, Spec. Rpt. Ser. No. 57. 159 pp.
752. Zeissler, J., and Rassfeld, L. 1928. Die anaerobe Sporen-
     flora der europäischen Kriegsschauplätze. 1917.
     Veröffentl. aus der Kriegs-und Konstitutionspathologie,
     5, Heft 2. 99 pp.

     The following contemporary publications should be
     noted, although of limited value to the historian:

753. Erikson, D. 1940. Pathogenic anaerobic organisms of the
     Actinomyces group. Great Britain, Med. Res. Council,
     Spec. Rpt. Ser. No. 240. 63 pp.
754. Hansen, A. U. 1950. Nogle Undersøgelser over Gramnega-
     tive Anaerobe Ikke-Spore-dannende Bacterier Isolereda fra
     Peritonsilloere Abscesser hos Mennesker. Ejnar Munds-
     gaard, Copenhagen, Denmark. 171 pp.
755. Hansen, K., Jeckeln, E., Jochims, H., Lezius, A., Meyer-
     Burgdorff, H., and Schutz, F. 1949. Darmbrand-Enteritis
     necroticans. Georg Thieme, Stuttgart, Germany. 212 pp.
756. Lebert, F., and Tardieux, P. 1952. Technique d'Isolement
     et de Détermination des Bactéries Anaérobies. 2d ed.
     Pacomhy, S.A.R.L., Paris. 55 pp. Techniques for iso-
     lation and species determination in Prevot's laboratory.
757. Prévot, A. R. 1948. Manuel de classification et de
     détermination des bactéries anaérobies. 2d ed. Masson
     et Cie, Paris. 290 pp. An excellent publication.
758. Smith, L. DS. 1955. Introduction to the pathogenic
     anaerobes. Univ. of Chicago Press. 253 pp. A mono-
     graph. Very valuable for practical information on
     anaerobic techniques. Excellent references at the end
     of each chapter.
759. Weinberg, M., Nativelle, R., and Prévot, A. R. 1937. Les
     microbes anaérobes. Masson et Cie, Paris. 1186 pp. A
     tremendous publication that evolved from Weinberg and
     Séguin's monograph.

REVIEWS

There are numerous contemporary reviews, but the following one is especially useful, for it indicates the major references and trends in this area of work:

769. McClung, L. S. 1956. The anaerobic bacteria with special
reference to the genus *Clostridium*. Ann Rev. Microbiol.,
10, 173–192.

See other sections, such as: Industrial; Insect; Petroleum; Physiology; Marine; Toxins; Food; Warfare; etc.

36

ANIMALS—EXPERIMENTAL USE

779. **Bibliography of Literature on the Necessity for Animal Experimentation.** Compiled by the office of the secretary of
the Illinois Society for Medical Research. Chicago, Ill.
A very fine bibliography. The following references by
Paget and Welch were found to be missing and are merely
added here:
780. Paget, S. 1903. Experiments on animals, with introduction
by Lord Lister. Murray, London.
781. _____. 1904. What we owe to experiments on animals.
The Scientific Press, London.
782. _____. 1912. For and against experiments on animals;
evidence before the Royal Commission on vivisection.
H. K. Lewis, London.
783. Welch, W. H. 1920. Papers and addresses. 3 vols. Medical education, history and miscellaneous, *vivisection*,
bibliography, index. The Johns Hopkins Press, Baltimore.
784. Bulletin, Illinois Soc. for Med. Research, No. 6. October,
1954. Chicago, Ill. Covers material published since
January 1, 1914 up to August 15, 1954. This is an excellent selective bibliography.
785. Keen, W. W. 1914. Animal experimentations and medical
progress. Houghton Miffin Co., Boston. Earlier literature on animal experimentations cited.
786. Root, W. S. 1957. The case for animal experimentation.
Trans. N. Y. Acad. Sciences, 19, 204–214. An excellent
summary, with historical development. Valuable references.

787. Stevenson, L. G. 1955. Science down the drain. On the hostility of certain sanitarians to animal experimentation, bacteriology and immunology. Bul. Hist. Med., 29, 1–26.

The following publications concerned with the care of laboratory animals have some references of historical importance:

788. Dumas, J. 1953. Les animaux de laboratoire (Anatomie, particularités physiologiques, hematologie, maladies naturelles, expérimentation). Flammarion, Paris. A rather complete list of references is found after each chapter. International in scope.

789. Symposium. 1941. Biology of the laboratory mouse. By the staff of the Roscoe B. Jackson Laboratory. Ed. by Snell, G. D., with a chapter on infectious diseases of mice by Dingle, J. H. The Blakiston Co., Philadelphia. A bibliography of 341 titles.

790. Symposium. 1949. The U. F. A. W. handbook on the care and management of laboratory animals. Ed. by Worden, A. N. Baillière, Tindall & Cox, London.

791. Symposium. 1949. The rat in laboratory investigation. Ed. by Farris, E. J., and Griffith, J. Q. 542 pp. A staff of twenty-nine contributors, with a useful contemporary bibliography, but of little historical value.

792. Symposium. 1950. The care and breeding of laboratory animals. Ed. by Farris, E. J. John Wiley & Sons, Inc., New York. 515 pp. A staff of fifteen contributors, with references at the ends of chapters. Some historical material found in some sections.

The five periodicals listed below often contain material of value on animal experimentation:

793. Bulletin of the Maryland Society for Medical Research, Inc. 1951–date. Baltimore.

794. Bulletin of the National Society for Medical Research. 1947–date. Chicago.

795. Bulletin of the New York State Society for Medical Research. 1952–date. New York.

796. Conquest. 1950–date. Research Defense Society, London.

797. ISMR Bulletin. 1952–date. Illinois Society for Medical Research, Chicago.

798. MRAC Reports. 1951–irregular. Medical Research Association of California, Los Angeles, Calif.

37

AUTOTROPHIC BACTERIA

808. **Symposium.** 1954. Autotrophic micro-organisms. Ed. by
Fry, B. A., and Peel, J. L. Fourth Symposium of the
Society for General Microbiology held at the Institution
of Electrical Engineers, London, April, 1954. Published
for the Society for General Microbiology at the Univ.
Press, Cambridge. 305 pp. This symposium is the best
single source for historical as well as contemporary
references. Numerous articles refer to the earlier literature and reviews. Although somewhat narrow in its
coverage (See review by Stanier, R. Y. 1955. Quart. Rev.
Biol., 30, 87), it is nevertheless an excellent source for
a beginning of a historical study. References to the following important earlier publications and reviews are
noted: Baas-Becking, M. G. (1925), Bavendamm, W.
(1924), Bunker, H. J. (1936), Cholodny, N. (1926),
Clifton, C. E. (1946, 1951), Edsden, S. R., (1952), Ellis,
D. (1932), Foster, J. W. (1951), Geitler, L., and Pascher,
A. (1925), Gest, H. (1951), Kluyer, A. J. (1931), Koffler,
H., and Wilson, P. W. (1951), Lockhead, A. G. (1952),
Lwoff, A. (1944), Meiklejohn, J. (1953), Molisch, H.
(1907, 1909), van Niel, C. B. (1935, 1943, 1941, 1944,
1949, 1952), Pringsheim, E. G. (1949, 1953), Stephenson,
M. (1949), Utter, M. F., and Wood, H. G. (1951), Umbreit,
W. W. (1947, 1951), Virtanen, A. I. (1948), Waksman, S.
A. (1927), Winogradsky, S. (1888), Zobell, C. E. (1946),
and others.

The contemporary reviews should not be overlooked for
historical material. Several reviews are noted for the best
historical sources available, for example:

809. **van Niel, C. B.** 1944. The culture, general physiology,
morphology, and classification of the non-sulphur purple
and brown bacteria. Bact. Rev., 8, 1–118 (162 ref.).
810. **Pringsheim, E. G.** 1949. The relationship between bacteria and Myxophyceae. Bact. Rev., 13, 47–98 (93 ref.).

38

BACTERIA—SPECIFIC ORGANISMS

There are numerous publications concerned with medical bacteriology that have references to the earlier literature, reviews, symposiums, etc., about specific organisms. One of the finest, with remarkable coverage of the literature, is:

820. **Wilson, G. S., and Miles, A. A.** 1955. Topley and Wilson's principles of bacteriology and immunity. 4th ed. The Williams & Wilkins Co., Baltimore. 2 vols. 2,331 pp.

In addition see, **General History; Actinomycetes; Anaerobic Bacteria; Autotrophic Bacteria; Classification, Food; Industrial; Insect; Marine; Petroleum; Plant Diseases; Soil; Spirochetes; etc.**

39

BACTERIOLOGY—CONTRIBUTIONS AND RELATIONSHIPS TO OTHER SCIENCES

830. **Bayne-Jones, S.** 1931. Reciprocal effects of the relationship of bacteriology and medicine. J. Bact., 21, 61–73.
831. **Hinshelwood, C. N.** 1949. Some relations between chemistry and biology. Blackwell Scientific Publications, Oxford.
832. **Kluyver, A. J., and van Niel, C. B.** 1956. The microbe's contribution to biology. Harvard Univ. Press. 182 pp. The authors present and interpret what they consider important contributions of microbiology to biology: Microbial metabolism, phototrophic bacteria (key to the understanding of green-plant photosynthesis), microbial adaptation, microbial mutations, and a stimulating chapter on "Evolution as viewed by the microbiologist." References following the chapters are of some historical importance.
833. **Kolmer, J. A.** 1927. The history of laboratory research in the past fifty years. Medical Life, 34, 3–14.

834. **Rettger, L. F.** 1918. The science of bacteriology and its relation to other sciences. J. Bact., 3, 103–113.
835. **Symposium.** 1955. Perspectives and horizons in microbiology. Ed. by Waksman, S. A. Rutgers Univ. Press. 220 pp. A very interesting symposium, with excellent historical material indicating some of the trends in bacteriology.
836. **Waksman, S. A.** 1943. The microbe as a biological system. J. Bact., 45, 1–10.

40

CHEMICAL AGENTS—HARMFUL EFFECT ON BACTERIA

846. **Buchanan, C. M.** 1895. Antisepsis and antiseptics. Terhume Co., Newark, N. J. 352 pp. An early classic.
847. **Bulloch, W.** 1938. The history of bacteriology. Oxford Univ. Press, London. See Section, "Bacteriological technique applied to the practice of chemical disinfection," pp. 235–236.
848. **Chick, H., and Browning, C. H.** 1930. The theory of disinfection. *In* A system of bacteriology in relation to medicine. Vol. 1., pp. 179–207. Excellent historical development. Pasteur, Lister, Esmarch, Henle, Fraenkel, Geppert, Behring, Koch.
849. **Dakin, H. D., and Dunham, E. K.** 1917. A handbook on antiseptics. The Macmillan Co., New York.
850. **McCulloch, E. C.** 1945. Disinfection and sterilization. 2d ed. Lea & Febiger, Philadelphia. 472 pp. A short section on history, pp. 15–22.
851. **Morton, L. T.** 1954. Garrison and Morton's medical bibliography. 2d ed. Argosy Bookstore, New York. See excellent listing of important historical references on antisepsis and asepsis, pp. 495–496, and on puerperal fever, pp. 548–549.
852. **Symposium.** 1954. Antiseptics, disinfectants, fungicides and chemical and physical sterilization. Ed. by Reddish, G. F. Lea & Febiger, Philadelphia. 841 pp. Historical

review by Reddish, G. F., pp. 13-20. Historical background of specific subjects given in individual chapters. (2d ed., 1957, 975 pp.)

FUNGICIDES

862. **Horsfall, J. G.** 1945. Fungicides and their action. Chronica Botanica Co., Waltham, Mass. Historical introduction, pp. 1-7. Excellent bibliography.

DDT

872. **Zimmerman, O. T., and Lavine, I.** 1946. DDT: Killer of killers. Industrial Research Service, Dover, N. H. 180 pp. An excellent historical account as well as the present outlook.

See section **Chemotherapy and Antibiotics** as well as numerous contemporary reviews and symposiums.

41

CHEMICAL COMPOSITION

882. **Baumgärtel, T.** 1924. Grundriss der theoretischen Bakteriologie. Berlin. An extensive summary of the early literature.
883. _____. 1928. The chemical structure of bacteria. *In* The newer knowledge of bacteriology and immunology. Ed. by Jordan, E. O., and Falk, I. S. The Univ. of Chicago Press. Earlier summary, pp. 14-18.
884. **Bracken, A.** 1954. Chemistry of micro-organisms. B. H. Blackwell, Oxford. 343 pp. References at the ends of chapters. An attempt at a historical introduction.
885. **Buchanan, R. W., and Fulmer, E. I.** 1928. Physiology and biochemistry of bacteria. Williams & Wilkins Co., Baltimore. Chapter III, in vol. 1, "Chemical composition of the cells of microörganisms," pp. 63-138. This is an excellent coverage of the earlier literature, with references.

886. **Porter, J. R.** 1946. Bacterial chemistry and physiology. John Wiley & Sons, Inc., New York. Chapter 5, "The chemical composition of microorganisms," pp. 352–450. This is one of the best available sources for contemporary, as well as historical, references.

42

CHEMOTHERAPY AND ANTIBIOTICS

BIBLIOGRAPHIES

896. **Annotated Bibliography.** 1943. Penicillin. Winthrop Chemical Co., Library, New York.
897. **Annotated Bibliographies.** Sulfaphridine, sulfathiazole, streptomycin, etc. Merck & Co., Inc., Rahway, N. J.
898. **Aureomycin, Bibliography and Index.** 1951. Lederle Lab., Div. American Cyanamid Co., New York. *Ibid.* The fifth year of aureomycin. 1952.
899. **Brochure with Bibliography.** 1945. Penicillin. Merck & Co., Rahway, N. J. (Supplement, 1946.)
900. **Handbook.** 1957. Handbook of toxicology. Vol. II (Antibiotics). W. B. Saunders Co., Philadelphia, Pa. 264 pp. Covers physical, chemical, biological, and toxicological properties of 340 important antibiotics.
901. **Hawking, F.,** and **Lawrence, J. S.** 1950. The sulphonamides. H. K. Lewis & Co., London. Over 1,000 references in the bibliography.
902. **Heyden Chemical Corp.,** New York. 1952. Neomycin; literature review and other pertinent data.
903. **Karel, L.,** and **Roach, E. S.** 1951. A dictionary and bibliography of antibiosis. Columbia Univ. Press, New York. 375 pp.
904. **Lewis, J. C.** 1950. Annotated bibliography of subtilin; assay, microbiological production, purification, and chemistry, biological activity, and related compounds. U. S. Dept. of Agriculture, Washington, D. C. 13 pp. Revision, August, 1952. 19 pp.

905. **Manual of Antibiotics.** (1954–1955.) 1954 ed. by Welch, H.
     Medical Encyclopedia, New York.
906. **Merck & Co.** 1942. Bacterial substances derived from
     micro-organisms. (Annotated bibliography.) Merck &
     Co., Rahway, N. J.
907. **Morton, L. T.** 1954. Garrison and Morton's medical bibli-
     ography. 2d ed. Argosy Bookstore, New York. Excellent
     listing of historical references, antibiotics, and sulphon-
     amides, pp. 168–171.
908. **Review.** 1951. Terramycin; review of the literature.
     Charles Pfizer & Co., Brooklyn, N. Y.
909. **Review.** 1952. Bacitracin. Research Division, S. B.
     Penick & Co., New York.
910. **Review.** 1953. The bacteriostatic activity of 3500 organic
     compounds for *Mycobacterium tuberculosis* var. *hominis.*
     Chem.-Biol. Coordination Center, Review No. 4.
     Youmans, G. P., Doub, L., and Youmans, A. S. National
     Research Council, Washington, D. C.
911. **Waksman, S. A.** 1952. The literature on streptomycin,
     1944–1952. Rutgers Univ. Press. 553 pp. A bibliography
     of 5,559 papers.
912. **Waksman, S. A.** *et al.* 1953. Neomycin: Nature, formation,
     isolation, and practical application. Rutgers Univ. Press.
     219 pp. Poor listing of references.
913. **Waksman, S. A., and Lechevalier, H. A.** 1953. Guide to
     the classification and identification of the Actinomycetes
     and their antibiotics. Williams & Wilkins Co., Baltimore.
     Selected general references, pp. 237–239. Includes de-
     tailed classification and descriptions of species.
914. **Whalley, M. E.** 1943. Abstracts on penicillin and other
     antibiotic substances. National Research Council of
     Canada, Ottawa. 71 pp. 2d ed., 1945. Reproduced
     from typewriting. 166 pp.
915. **Journal: Antibiotics.** 1951-date. Published by Pharma-
     ceutical Society of Great Britain. Reviews articles with
     bibliographies; includes history.

HISTORY

925. **Bustinza Lachiondo, F.** 1945. De Pasteur a Fleming: los
     antibioticos antimicrobianos y la penicelina. 2d ed.

Editorial plus-ultra, Madrid. Sections on bacteria, molds, chemotherapy, and antibiotics.

926. Domagk, G., and Hegler, C. 1944. Chemotherapie Bakterieller Infektionen. Beiträge zur Arzneimitteltherapie. Band I. 3d ed. J. W. Edwards, Ann Arbor, Mich. Excellent history of the development of sulfonamide therapy.

927. Duthie, E. S. 1946. Molecules against microbes. Sigma Books, London.

928. Ehrlich, P., and Hata, S. 1910. Die experimentelle Chemotherapie d. Spirillosen, Berlin.

929. Epstein, S., and Williams, B. 1946. Miracles from microbes; the road to streptomycin. With an introduction by Kirk, N. T. Rutgers Univ. Press, New Brunswick, N. J. 155 pp. Two chapters devoted to the early development of streptomycin, as well as information on tyrothricin, penicillin, and streptomycin. A popular and well-written book on the history of antibiotics.

930. Findlay, G. M. 1950. Recent advances in chemotherapy. 2 vols. The Blakiston Co., Philadelphia. History of chemotherapy, pp. 1–15, with references. Tremendous listing of references.

931. Fleming, A. 1946. Penicillin. Its practical application. The Blakiston Co., Philadelphia. Short history, pp. 1–23.

932. _____. 1946. Chemotherapy: yesterday, today, and tomorrow. Cambridge Univ. Press, London. 39 pp. An excellent short historical review. "Who is there who could have told the tale better?"

933. Florey, H. W., and Abraham, E. P. 1951. The work on penicillin at Oxford. Jour. Hist. Med., 6, 302–316.

934. Florey, Sir Howard. 1951. Antibiotics, being the fifty-second Robert Boyle lecture delivered before the Oxford Univ. Scientific Club of June 1, 1951. C. C Thomas, Springfield, Ill.

935. Florey, Sir Howard (et al.). 1949. Antibiotics: a survey of penicillin, streptomycin, and other antimicrobial substances from fungi, Actinomycetes, bacteria, and plants. 2 vols. Oxford Univ. Press, London. A remarkable survey of the historical laboratory investigations is included in this work. Historical introduction by Florey, H. W., vol. I, pp. 1–37; by Abraham, E. P., Chain, E., et. al., vol. II, pp. 631–671.

936. Gaw, H. Z., and Wang, H. P. 1949. Survey of Chinese drugs for presence of antibacterial substances. Science, 110, 11–12.

937. Gladston, I. 1940. Some notes on the early history of chemotherapy. Bul. Hist. Med., 8, 806–818.

938. _____. 1943. Behind the sulfa drugs: a short history of chemotherapy. D. Appleton-Century Co., New York. 174 pp. A survey of the development of chemotherapy. No bibliography.

939. _____. (ed.). 1958. The impact of the antibiotics on medicine and society. Mongr. II. Inst. of Social and Historical Med. International Univ. Press, N. Y. 232 pp.

940. Guthrie, D. 1955. From witchcraft to antisepsis: a study in antithesis. Univ. of Kansas Press. 53 pp. (A Logan Clendening Lecture on the history and philosophy of medicine, 5th series.) Lessons to be learned of interest and value to modern medicine.

941. Goldsmith, M. 1946. The road to penicillin, a history of chemotherapy. Lindsay Drummond, London.

942. Havinga, E., Julius, H. W., Veldstra, H., and Winkler, K. C. 1946. Modern development of chemotherapy. Elsevier Publishing Co., Inc., New York and Amsterdam. Introduction and historical development, pp. 1–9; bacteriological investigations, pp. 10–11.

943. Herrell, W. E. 1945. Penicillin and other antibiotic agents. W. B. Saunders Co., Philadelphia. 348 pp. An interesting chapter has been written on the historical aspects of the development of pencillin, a history to which he himself contributed.

944. Hobby, G. L. 1951. Microbiology in relation to antibiotics. Jour. His. Med. 6, 369–378.

945. Jaramillo-Arango, J. 1953. The British contribution to medicine. Foreword by Sir Authur MacNalty. E. & S. Livingstone, Edinburgh. 266 pp. An important chapter on the history of antibiotics.

946. Landsberg, H. 1949. Prelude to the discovery of pencillin. Apropos of Tyndall, 1881.

947. Landgon-Brown, W. 1941. From witchcraft to chemotherapy. Cambridge Univ. Press, London. 60 pp. A brief history.

948. Lawrence, J. S., and Francis, J. 1953. The sulphonamides and antibiotics in man and animals. H. K. Lewis & Co.,

Ltd., London. Short section on history in introduction, pp. 1-8; references, pp. 432-472.

949. Long, P. H., and Bliss, E. A. 1939. The clinical and experimental use of sulfanilamide, sulfaphridine, and allied compounds. The Macmillan Co., New York. Short history, pp. 1-13.

950. Masters, D. 1946. Miracle drug. The inner history of penicillin. Eyre and Spottiswoode, London. 191 pp.

951. Morton, L. T. 1954. Garrison and Morton's medical bibliography. An annotated check-list of texts illustrating the history of medicine. 2d ed. Printed by W. J. Rawlinson, Ltd., Netherlands. See sections, Antibiotics, pp. 168-170; Sulphonamides, pp. 170-171, and several important historical references in section Material Medica: Pharmacy: Pharmacology, pp. 155-170.

952. Narriott, H. J. L. 1953. Medical milestones. William & Wilkins Co., Baltimore. 293 pp. An interesting popular account of antibiotics and other areas.

953. Neisser, A. (1855-1916.) 1944. On modern syphilotherapy, with particular reference to salvarsan. Biography and bibliography by Gardner, F. T. Bul. Hist. Med., 16, 469-510.

954. Neisser, A. 1945. On modern syphilotherapy, with particular reference to salvarsan. Transl. by von Sazenhofen Wartenberg, I. The Johns Hopkins Univ. Press, Baltimore. 42 pp. A reprinted essay of 1911; is one of the first based on the use of Ehrlich's famous 606.

955. Northey, E. J. 1948. The sulfonamides and allied compounds. Amer. Chem. Soc. Monograph Series. Reinhold Publishing Corp., New York. 600 pp. A historical review of the subject is presented in Chapter 1. Over 2,600 references, largely chemical.

956. Our Smallest Servants: The Story of Fermentation. 1956. Charles Pfizer & Co., Brooklyn, N. Y. A short historical introduction to the subject.

957. Penicillin. 1947. The chemical study of penicillin; a brief history. Science, 105, 653-659.

958. Ratcliff, J. D. 1940. Men against microbes. Harrolds, London.

959. _____. 1945. Yellow magic. The story of penicillin. Random House, New York. 173 pp. An excellent historical "popular" account of chemotherapy.

960. Rettger, L. F., and Cheplin, H. A. 1921. The transforma-
tion of intestinal flora, with special reference to the
implanation of *Bacillus acidophilis*. Yale Univ. Press.

961. Schmitzer, R. J., and Grunberg, E. 1957. Drug resistance
of microorganisms. Academic Press, Inc., New York. 395
pp. An attempt to connect the past experience with the
present. Excellent references.

962. Silverman, M. 1948. Magic in a bottle. 2d ed. The Macmillan Co., New York. Several chapters of interest to
bacteriologists, such as "Lister to Ehrlich to 205;
Domagk and the sulfa-drugs; Fleming, Florey and penicillin." Excellent bibliography.

963. Sokoloff, B. 1945. The story of penicillin. Ziff-Davis
Publishing Co., Chicago. 167 pp. A book intermediate
between a popular exposition and a general technical
account. Chapters on Pasteur and Ehrlich. Bibliography,
pp. 143–160.

964. Sophian, L. H., Piper, D. L., and Schneller, G. H. 1952.
The sulfapyrimidines. A. Colish, New York. A very
short history, pp. 10–14.

965. Symposium. 1946. Antibiotics. Part I: Microbiological;
Part II: Pharmacological. Annals. N. Y. Acad. Sciences,
48, 31–218. Waksman presents some historical information regarding the basic concept of antibiosis.

966. Symposium. 1949. Antibiotics derived from *Bacillus
polymyxa.* Ann. N. Y. Acad. Sciences, 51, 853–1000.
Historical aspects by Stansley, P. G., pp. 835–856.

967. Symposium. 1949. The chemistry of penicillin. Ed. by
Clarke, H. T., Johnson, J. R., and Robinson, R. Prince-
ton Univ. Press. Brief history of chemical studies in
Chapter I; the earlier investigations of the penicillius,
through December, 1943, are dealt with in Chapters II,
III, and IV.

968. Taylor, F. S. 1942. The conquest of bacteria (from Salvarsan to sulphapyridine). Philosophical Library, New
York. 175 pp. Very brief review of bacteriology. Brief
sketches on the rise of chemotherapy. Originally published in 1940. The conquest of bacteria from 606 to
693. 2d ed. Secker & Warburg, London. 144 pp.

969. Urdang, G. 1951. The antibiotics and pharmacy. Jour.
Hist. Med., 6, 388–405.

970. **Waksman, S. A.** 1937. Associative and antagonistic effects of microörganisms. I. Historical review of antagonistic relationships. Soil Sci., 43, 51–68.

971. _____. 1947. Microbial antagonism and antibiotic substances. 2d ed. The Commonwealth Fund, Waltham, Mass. 415 pp. First edition, 1945, is superior to the second owing to the omission in the latter of a number of references concerning historical interests.

972. _____. 1951. Streptomycin. Isolation, properties, and utilizations. Jour. Hist. Med., 6, 318–347.

973. _____. 1953. Neomycin. Rutgers Univ. Press. Historical background, pp. vii–ix. Literature on neomycin, pp. 198–211.

974. **Welch, H.** 1951. Pharmacology of antibiotics. Jour. His. Med., 6, 348–368.

975. **Welsch, M.** 1946. S. A. Waksman et la streptomycine. Rev. médicale de Liege, 1, 180–183.

976. _____. 1950. De l'origine et de la signification du terme "antibiotique." III-e Congrès National des Sciences, 59–62. Bruxelles.

977. **Wolley, D. W.** 1952. A study of antimetabolites. John Wiley & Sons, Inc., New York.

978. **Work, T. S.,** and **Work, E.** 1948. The basis of chemotherapy. Interscience Publishers, Inc., New York. Historical introduction, pp. 1–39; bibliography, pp. 363–416. This is an excellent, skillful blending of chemical theory, enzymology, cell physiology, and bacteriology.

43

CLASSIFICATION

The historian should refer to the systems of classification developed after 1773. These are given in complete outline form in the first edition of Bergey's Manual (1923). This was reprinted in the second (1925) and third (1930) editions without material changes.

987. **Bergey, D. H., Harrison, F. C., Breed, R. S., Hammer, B. W.,**
and **Huntoon, F. M.** 1923. Bergey's manual of determinative bacteriology. Williams & Wilkins Co., Baltimore.
Introduction, pp. 1–28. The classification of bacteria by
early writers. References given. Excellent presentation.
Historical references found in the 6th ed., 1948, but without the complete outlines as found in previous editions.
Note historical references such as: Müller (1786), Ehren-
berg (1838), Dujardin (1841), Nägeli (1857), Devaine
(1868), Hoffmann (1869), Cohn (1875), Magnin (1878),
Winter (1881), Burrill (1882), Zopf (1880–1885), Flügge
(1886), Hueppe (1886), Baumgarten (1890), Sternberg
(1892), Lehmann and Neumann (1896), Fischer (1897),
Migula (1900), Chester (1901), Smith, E. (1905), Winslow
(1908), Orla-Jensen (1919), Buchanan (1915–1917),
Castellani and Chalmers (1919), and The Committee on
Characterization and Classification of the Society of
American Bacteriologists (1917–1920).

988. **Buchanan, R. E.** 1925. General systematic bacteriology.
Monograph of systematic bacteriology. Williams &
Wilkins Co., Baltimore. 597 pp. History, pp. 15–108,
with extensive bibliography.

989. **Bulloch, W.** 1930. The history of bacteriology. *In* A system of bacteriology. Medical Research Council, H.M.S.O.,
London. Vol. 1. Section: "Classification of bacteria:
discovery of anthrax bacillus; Fungoid theory; Hallier;
Researches of Cohn, Billroth, Zopf; Later systems of
classification." Excellent listing of references, pp. 58–
66.

990. _____. 1938. The history of bacteriology. Oxford
Univ. Press, London. Outstanding discussion on the
history of classification of bacteria, pp. 171–203; references, pp. 317–327.

991. **Cohn, F.** 1872. Bacteria, the smallest of living organisms.
Transl. by Dolley, C. S. Introduction by Leikind, M. C.
1939. The Johns Hopkins Press, Baltimore. 44 pp.
Ferdinand Cohn did much to aid in the establishment of
bacteriology as a branch of science. Bibliography of
Ferdinand Cohn, pp. 40–44. A historical classic which in
a masterly fashion sketches the early history of the study
of microbes.

992. **Elliott, C.** 1951. Manual of bacterial plant pathogens. 2d ed. A Chronica Botanica Publication. The Ronald Press Co., New York. 186 pp. The "bible" for plant pathogens.
993. **Ford, W. W.** 1939. Bacteriology. Paul B. Hoeber, Inc., New York. A very brief history of taxonomy of bacteria, pp. 143–145.
994. **Perkins, R. G.** 1928. Classification of bacteria. *In* The newer knowledge of bacteriology and immunology. Ed. by Jordan, E. O., and Falk, I. S. Univ. of Chicago Press. Pp. 120–135. A short historical development with a select list of references.
995. **Pribram, E.** 1933. Klassifikation der Schizomyceten (Bakterien) Versuch einer wissenschaftlichen Klassifikation der Bakterien auf botanischer Grundlage. Deuticke, Leipzig.

A journal of importance:

996. **International Bulletin of Bacteriological Nomenclature and Taxonomy.** Vol. 1. 1951-date. Iowa State College Press, Ames, Iowa. Official organ of the International Committee on Bacteriological Nomenclature of the International Association of Microbiologists and Its Judicial Commission.
    1. Bacteria—Classification—Period.
    2. Bacteriology. Nomenclature—Period.
    3. International Association of Microbiologists. International Committee on Bacteriological Nomenclature.

The following two reviews may have some special interest:

997. **Dienes, L., and Weinberger, H. J.** 1951. The L forms of bacteria. Bact. Revs., 15, 284–288. Short historical introduction with 94 references.
998. **van Niel, C. B.** 1944. The culture, general physiology, morphology, and classification of the non-sulfur purple and brown bacteria. Bact. Revs., 8, 1–118. Excellent historical development with 162 references.

Also see sections such as **Actinomycetes, Anaerobic Bacteria, Autotrophic Bacteria, Bacteria—Specific Organisms, Insect, Marine, Viruses, Chemotherapy and Antibiotics.**

44

CULTIVATION AND IDENTIFICATION

1008. **Bulloch, W.** 1930. The history of bacteriology. *In* A system of bacteriology. Medical Research Council, H. M. S. O., London. Vol. 1. Section, "Development of Bacteriological Technique: Researches of Robert Koch and Pasteur," pp. 67–85.

1009. ———. 1938. The history of bacteriology. Oxford Univ. Press, London. Section, "Cultivation of Bacteria," pp. 207–238. References, pp. 327–335. This is an outstanding presentation.

In addition, the following are useful but limited:

1010. **Chapman, V. J.** 1949. Seaweeds and their uses. Pitman Publishing Corp., New York. 287 pp. Appendix illustrated, 20 pp. Section on agar-agar, pp. 89–123.

1011. **Levine, M., and Schoenlein, H. W.** 1930. A compilation of culture media. For the cultivation of microorganisms. The Williams & Wilkins Co., Baltimore. 969 pp. Extensive list of references, pp. 915–969. Excellent indexes.

1012. **Manual.** Culture media, materials and apparatus for the bacteriological laboratory. 1948. Baltimore Biological Laboratories, Inc., Baltimore. Use for U. S. A.

1013. **Manual of Dehydrated Culture Media and Reagents.** 1953. Difco Laboratories, Detroit, Mich. References of historical importance at the end of each section. Useful for U. S. A.

1014. **Manual of Microbiological Methods.** 1957. By the Society of American Bacteriologists. Pelczar, M. J., Jr. (Chairman). McGraw-Hill Book Co., Inc., New York. 315 pp. References at end of each section.

1015. **Simon, S.** 1907. Geschichte der Reinkultur. München. History of pure culture.

Contemporary references of value:

1016. **Hallmann, L.** 1953. Bakteriologische Nährböden, ausgewählte Nährbodenrezepturen für das medizinisch-bakteriologische Laboratorium. G. Thieme, Stuttgart. 252 pp.

1017. **Hauduroy, P.** 1951. Techniques bactériologiques utilisées pour l'isolement, la détermination et la conservation des microorganismes. (Bactéries, champignons, microscopiques, virus.) Masson et Cie, Paris. 168 pp. An alphabetical arrangement of culture media and a brief description of microbiological procedures. Valuable reference regarding French techniques and methods.

1018. **McClung, L. S.** 1949. Recent developments in microbiological techniques. Ann. Rev. Microbiol., 3, 395–422.

TECHNIQUES FOR ISOLATION OF SINGLE MICROORGANISMS

1028. **Hildebrand, E. M.** 1938. Technique for the isolation of single microorganisms. Bot. Rev., 4, 627–664. (1950. Bot. Rev., 16, 181–207.)

VIRUSES

1038. **Beveridge, W. I. B.,** and **Burnet, F. M.** 1946. The cultivation of viruses and rickettsiae in the chick embryo. H. M. S. O., London. 92 pp. Excellent historical introduction; references, pp. 80–92.

Also see sections on **Classification, Staining, Microscope.**

45

DAIRY

To the author's knowledge, there appears to be no writing devoted specifically to the history of this area of bacteriology.

1048. **Breed, R. S.** 1928. Bacteria in milk. *In* The newer knowledge of bacteriology and immunity. Ed. by Jordan, E. O., and **Falk, I. S. Univ. of Chicago Press.** Pp. 378–394. Important historical references are listed. This is a source for future work.

1049. **Moore, V. A.** 1902. Bacteria in milk. J. B. Lyon Co., Albany. 28 pp. An early introduction.

There are numerous textbooks on dairy bacteriology, but few even list references and hardly ever approach any aspects of it from the historical viewpoint. Two of the better sources, of some help, are:

1050. Foster, E. M., Nelson, F. E., Speck, M. L., Doetsch, R. N., and Olson, J. C. 1957. Dairy microbiology. Prentice-Hall, Inc., Englewood Cliffs, N. J. 492 pp.

1051. Hammer, B. W. 1948. Dairy bacteriology. 3d ed. John Wiley & Sons, Inc., New York. 593 pp. References of some value are given at the ends of chapters. (4th ed. by Hammer, B. W., and Babel, F. J. 1957. 623 pp.)

In addition, see:

1052. Bulloch, W. 1938. The history of bacteriology. Oxford Univ. Press, London. 422 pp. See work of Pasteur.

1053. Orla-Jensen, S. 1942. The lactic acid bacteria. 2d ed. I Kommission Hos Ejnar Munksgaard, København. 196 pp.

1054. Tittsler, R. P. 1952. Introduction to and symposium on the lactic acid bacteria. Bact. Revs., 16, 227–260.

1055. Abstracts of Literature, Milk and Milk Products. 1936–date. Published monthly in Jour. Dairy Science.

1056. Dairy Science Abstracts. 1939–date. Commonwealth Agricultural Bureaus Publication.

46

DENTAL

The history of dental bacteriology is closely associated with the history of medical bacteriology. Bulloch's references should therefore be consulted.

1066. Appleton, J. L. T. 1950. Bacterial infection with special reference to dental practice. 4th ed. Lea & Febiger, Philadelphia. 644 pp. Although this text is designed primarily for dental students and dentists, it is nevertheless a useful source for information concerned with oral hygiene.

1067. Burnett, G. W., and Scherp, H. W. 1957. Oral microbiology and infectious disease. Williams & Wilkins Co., Baltimore. 589 pp. A brief but excellent history of the development of oral microbiology, pp. 3–33.

1068. **Miller, W. D.** 1890. The micro-organisms of the human mouth. S. S. White Dental Mfg. Co., Philadelphia. 364 pp. This is the early classic in this field. Miller greatly advanced the knowledge of dental bacteriology. His book first appeared in a German edition in 1889.

Reviews: The following reviews, although of contemporary interest, should also be consulted:

1069. **Harrison, R. W.** 1949. Oral microbiology. Ann Rev. Microbiol., 3, 317–330.
1070. **Hoffman, H.** 1957. Oral microbiology. Ann. Rev. Microbiol., 11, 183–198.
1071. **Rosebury, T.** 1944. The parasitic actinomycetes and other filamentous microörganisms of the mouth. Bact. Revs., 8, 189–223.
1072. **Toverud, G., Finn, S. B., Cox, G. J.,** and **Bodecker, C. F.** 1952. A survey of the literature of dental caries. Natl. Acad. Sci.—Natl. Research Council, Washington, D. C. 567 pp.

In addition, one should refer to various publications concerned with the history of dentistry, such as:

1073. **Morton, L. T.** 1954. Garrison and Morton's medical bibliography. 2d ed. Argosy Bookstore, New York. Pp. 320–323.
1074. **Sarton, G.** 1952. Horus. A guide to the history of science. A Chronica Botanica Publication. The Ronald Press Co., New York. Refer to p. 189 for a listing of books on the history of dentistry.
1075. **Sigerist, H. E.** 1951. A history of medicine. Oxford Univ. Press. See listings on history of dentistry, p. 502.

47

ECOLOGY—BACTERIAL

The following publications are listed but admittedly some are of little historical value:

1085. **Baumgärtel, T.** 1946. Mikrobielle Symbiosen in Pflanzen- und Tierreich. Die Wissenschaft, Band 94. (Friedr. Vieweg & Sohn, Braunschweig.) J. W. Edwards, Ann

Arbor. 132 pp. Bacterial symbioses dominate and fungus symbioses come next.

1086. **Burkholder, P. R.** 1952. Cooperation and conflict among primitive organisms. Amer. Scientist, 40, 601–631.

1087. **Symposium.** 1954. Adaptation in micro-organisms. Ed. by Gale, E. F., and Davies, R. Cambridge Univ. Press. 339 pp. This is the third symposium of the Society for General Microbiology, held at The Royal Institution, London, April, 1953, and published for the Society. There are valuable references found in this symposium, although it is a heterogeneous and confusing publication.

1088. **Symposium.** 1957. Microbial ecology. Cambridge Univ. Press. 388 pp. This is the seventh symposium of the Society for General Microbiology held at the Royal Institution, London, April, 1957. This is the first attempt at a comprehensive treatment of microbial ecology. It lists numerous important references.

1089. **Walfenbarger, D. O.** 1946. Dispersion of small organisms, distance dispersion rates of bacteria, spores, seeds, pollen, and insects. Incidence rates of diseases and injury. The American Midland Naturalist, Vol. 35, No. 1. The Univ. of Notre Dame Press. 152 pp. A bibliography of some 230 titles.

1090. **Winogradsky, S. N.** 1949. Microbiologie du sol, problèmes et methodes. Cinquante Ans de Recherches. Masson et Cie, Paris. 861 pp. One of the great publications in methodology and ecology.

See sections on **Autotrophic Bacteria, Soil.**

48

ENZYMES—BACTERIAL

1100. **Porter, J. R.** 1946. Bacterial chemistry and physiology. John Wiley & Sons, Inc., New York. 1073 pp. Chapter 6, "Bacterial enzymes and bacterial respiration," pp. 451–614, has an extensive bibliography with excellent historical material.

1101. **Waksman, S. A.,** and **Davison, W. C.** 1926. Enzymes. Williams & Wilkins Co., Baltimore. 364 pp. Contains a very short historical introduction. Bibliography of 1323 references.

There are numerous contemporary reviews that one should refer to, such as: Biol. Rev., Bact. Rev., Ann. Rev. Microbiol., Advances in Enzymology, etc.

49

EPIDEMIOLOGY

See excellent listings in the following publications:

1111. **Bett, W. R. (ed.).** 1954. The history and conquest of common diseases. Univ. of Oklahoma Press. 334 pp. Several sections of interest to the medical bacteriologist. Excellent references.

1112. **Doe, J.,** and **Marshall, M. L.** (eds.). 1956. Handbook of medical library practice. 2d ed. Amer. Library Assoc. Chicago. See excellent listings concerned with public health, epidemiology, hygiene, sanitation, pp. 502–509.

1113. **Duffy, J.** 1953. Epidemics in colonial America. Louisiana State Univ. Press. 274 pp. Sources of references, pp. 249–264.

1114. **Morton, L. T.** 1954. Garrison and Morton's medical bibliography. An annotated check-list of texts illustrating the history of medicine. 2d ed. Printed by W. J. Rawlinson, Ltd., Netherlands. See section, epidemiology, pp. 146–147.

1115. **Pauly, A.** 1954. Bibliographie des sciences médicales. Derek Verschoyle, Academic and Bibliographical Publishers, Ltd., London. 1758 pp. See section, Histoire des epidemies, pp. 1319–1555.

1116. **Sarton, G.** 1952. Horus. A guide to the history of science. A Chronica Botanica Publication. The Ronald Press Co., New York. P. 189.

1117. **Stallybrass, C. O.** 1931. The principles of epidemiology and the process of infection. The Macmillan Co., New

York. 696 pp. Selective bibliography, pp. 655–680.
Unfortunately by authors only.

1118. **Winslow, C.-E. A., Smillie, W. G., Doull, J. A., and
Gordon, J. E.** 1952. The history of American epidemiology. C. V. Mosby Co., St. Louis. 190 pp. Note section by Doull, J. A., The bacteriological era (1876–
1920), pp. 74–113, with listing of references.

The following classics are of great interest to the bacteriologist:

1119. **Budd, W.** 1873. Typhoid fever; its nature, mode of spread-
ing, and prevention. Longmans, Green & Co., London.
Reprinted, 1931. Delta Omega Soc., Amer. Publ. Health
Assoc., New York.

1120. **Semmelweis, I. P.** 1941. Medical Classics, 5, 338–775.
Biography, bibliography. First translation into English
of the entire book on childbed fever.

1121. **Snow, J.** 1936. On cholera. Reprint of two papers. The
Commonwealth Fund, New York. 191 pp.

50

FOOD

1131. **Jensen, L. B.** 1954. Microbiology of meats. 3d ed. The
Garrard Press, Publishers, Champaign, Ill. 422 pp.
Deals with the industrial microbiology of meat foods.
Chapter 1, a brief introduction and history, with 16 references. Other references found in each chapter. This is
an excellent coverage of the field, with a brief historical development in each chapter.

1132. **Tanner, F. W.** 1944. The microbiology of foods. 2d ed.
Garrard Press, Champaign, Ill. 1,196 pp. A tremendous
volume, with references at the bottom of the pages and a
list of reference books at the ends of chapters. A concise chapter on history, however, is needed.

FOOD POISONING

1142. **Dewberry, E. B.** 1950. Food poisoning. Its nature, history and causation; measures for its prevention and con-

trol. Foreword by Leighton, G. R. Leonard Hill, Ltd.,
London. 315 pp. Chapter II, pp. 4-16, including excellent list of references. This is the finest short presentation on the history of this subject. It includes photographs of Savage, Smith, T., Gaertner, McWeeney,
Ballard, Tanner, White, P. B., Durham, Jordan, and
Beveridge. Other photographs in other areas of the book.
There is a selective bibliography at the end of the book
which includes such publications as:

Clayton, E. C. 1909. Compendium of food microscopy.
Baillière, Tindall & Cox, England. 472 pp.

Damon, S. R. 1928. Food infections and intoxications. Baillière, Tindall & Cox, England.

Graham-Smith. 1914. Flies in relation to disease.
Out of print.

Jordan, E. O. 1931. Food poisoning and food-borne
infections. Univ. of Chicago Press, Chicago.

Leighton, G. 1923. Botulism and preservation.
Collins, England.

And numerous books on fungi, sanitation, and public
health.

FOOD-BORNE INFECTIONS

1152. Tanner, F. W., and Tanner, L. P. 1953. Food-borne infections and intoxications. 2d ed. The Garrard Press,
Publishers, Champaign, Ill. 769 pp. Numerous references given at the bottom of the page. A basis for a
historical discussion is in this book but would require
considerable work.

51

GENETICS, VARIATION, EVOLUTION

The bacteriologist should be well acquainted with the
history of general genetics. The following publications
have been found of great value:

1162. Dobzhansky, Th. 1941. Genetics and the origin of
species. 2d ed. Columbia Univ. Press. 446 pp. One

of the most significant books since Darwin's "Origin of Species."

1163. **Dunn, L. C.** (ed.). 1951. Genetics in the 20th century; essays on the progress of genetics during its first 50 years. The Macmillan Co., New York. 634 pp. Excellent history before 1900, genetics and immunology, genetic studies in bacteria, genetics and disease resistance, and genetics and the cancer problem of interest to the bacteriologist. Excellent bibliography.

1164. **Morton, L. T.** 1954. Garrison and Morton's medical bibliography. 2d ed. Argosy Bookstore, New York. See excellent listing of historical references on evolution, heredity, genetics, pp. 21–24.

1165. **Sinnott, E. W., Dunn, L. C., and Dobzhansky, Th.** 1958. Principles of genetics. The McGraw-Hill Book Co., Inc., New York. 459 pp. First section serves as an introduction and as a history. All chapters have a historical approach. Excellent bibliography.

1166. **Zirkle, C.** 1941. Natural selection before the "Origin of Species." Proc. Amer. Philosophical Soc., 84, 71–123. Note Buffon (1751).

1167. _____. 1946. The early history of the idea of the inheritance of acquired characters and of pangenesis. Trans. Amer. Philosophical Soc., 35, 91–151.

1168. _____. 1951. Gregor Mendel and his precursors. Isis, 42, 97–104. "Mendel's experiments were so much more extensive and precise than those which went before that we are still justified in crediting him as the founder of a science."

BACTERIAL GENETICS

In the earlier bacteriological writings there will be found but few references that deviated from the idea of fixity of species rather than variability. During the last twenty-five years the relevant literature has expanded from a trickle to a flood. With few exceptions, bacterial genetics does not start until early in 1940. Braun's book, as well as Wilson and Miles', listed below, will refer the reader to numerous important reviews, symposiums, and other references of contemporary importance. In addition, see Cavalli-Sforza, L. L. 1957. Bacterial genetics. Ann. Rev. Microbiol., 11, 391–418.

1178. **Arkwright, J. A.** 1930. Variation, *In* A system of bacteriology in relation to medicine. Vol. 1, pp. 311–374.
Excellent historical development. The references list
such important books of historical importance as:
Calmette, A. (1922), Enderlein, G. (1925), d'Herelle, F.
(1922), Hueppe (1885), Kolle, W. and Prigge, R. (1928),
v. Naegele, C. (1882), Stewart, F. H. (1927), and
Wasserman, A. V., and Keysser, F. (1912).

1179. **Braun, W.** 1953. Bacterial genetics. W. B. Saunders Co.,
Philadelphia. 238 pp. See Chapter 2, "The evolution
of bacterial genetics," pp. 32–37. Although this chapter
is far too short, it is nevertheless an excellent summary
of the historical development of bacterial genetics. Important references are listed. Note the Koch-Cohn era
(1881) of extreme monomorphism. The "cyclogenic"
theory advanced by Enderlein, Mellon, Hadley, and
others. The contemporary period of 1940, with tremendous changes. Excellent references.

1180. **Bulloch, W.** 1938. The history of bacteriology. Oxford
Univ. Press, London. This is an excellent source for
references to the earlier work on bacterial variation.

1181. **Henrici, A. J.** 1928. Morphologic variation and the rate
of growth of bacteria. C. C Thomas, Publishers, Springfield, Ill. 194 pp. A classic monograph concerning the
earlier studies on morphological variations. Good listing of references in Appendix, pp. 177–185.

1182. **Lederberg, J.** 1956. Genetic transduction. Amer. Scient.,
44, 264–280. An excellent historical account of the
recent advances in the genetics of bacteria and, incidentally, of recent advances in genetic theory.

1183. **Wilson, G. S.,** and **Miles, A. A.** 1955. Topley and
Wilson's principles of bacteriology and immunity. 4th
ed. Williams & Wilkins Co., Baltimore. Vol. 1. See
Chapter 9, "Variation and inheritance in bacteria,"
pp. 335–369. An excellent review with an extensive
list of references.

1184. **Winogradsky, S.** 1937. The doctrine of pleomorphism in
bacteriology. Soil Sci., 43, 327–340. The best and
most authoritative historical summary on the doctrine of
pleomorphism in bacteriology.

1185. Yura, T. 1956. Genetic studies with bacteria. Carnegie
　　　Institute of Washington, Publ. 612, Washington, D. C.
　　　136 pp.

52

GERM-FREE TECHNIQUES

1195. **Glimstedt, G.** 1936. Bakterienfreie Meerschweinchen.
　　　Aüfzucht, Lebensfähigkeit und Wachstum, nebst Unter-
　　　suchungen über das lymphatische Gewebe. Levin und
　　　Munksgaard, Copenhagen. 295 pp. Numerous attempts
　　　have been made to rear bacteria-free animals since 1885.
　　　This is an important book on bacteria-free techniques.
　　　A 13-page bibliography is provided and is of historical
　　　importance.

　　　Contemporary publications such as the following should
　　　be noted:

1196. **Reyniers, J. A.** 1943. Micurgical and germ free tech-
　　　niques. C. C Thomas, Publishers, Springfield, Ill.
　　　162 pp. References follow each chapter.
1197. _____. (ed.). Germ free life studies. Univ. of
　　　Notre Dame, Notre Dame, Ind. No. 1 (No. 2, 1949).
　　　120 pp. Important references, pp. 116–120.

53

GROWTH AND DEATH

1207. **Monod, J.** 1942. Recherches sur la croissance des cul-
　　　tures bactériennes. Herman et Cie, Paris. 211 pp.
　　　This is an excellent review for historical material.
1208. **Porter, J. R.** 1946. Bacterial chemistry and physiology.
　　　John Wiley & Sons, Inc., New York. Pp. 93–143.
1209. **Slator, A., Gardner, A. P.,** and **Thornton, H. G.** 1930.
　　　Growth and reproduction of bacteria. *In* A system of

bacteriology in relation to medicine. Vol. 1, pp. 145–178. Excellent historical development with references.

1210. **Symposium.** 1956. The biology of ageing. Hafner Publishing Co., New York. 128 pp. A noteworthy chapter by Hinshelwood, C., "Ageing in bacteria."

Although the following publication is mentioned in the above sources, it is well to repeat here:

1211. **Löhnis, F.** 1922. Studies upon the life cycle of bacteria. (Review of the literature, 1839–1918.) National Academy of Sciences. Memoirs, Vol. 16, No. 2. Washington, D. C.

54

IMMUNOLOGY AND SEROLOGY

1221. **Bulloch, W.** 1930. The history of bacteriology. *In* A system of bacteriology. Medical Research Council, H. M. S. O., London. Vol. 1. There are two sections that are concerned with the history of immunology: "Researches of Pasteur on attenuation of virus and prophylactic inoculation," pp. 79–85, and "History of immunity doctrines," pp. 85–103. Both have excellent listings of references.

1222. _____. 1938. The history of bacteriology. Oxford Univ. Press, London. Chapter X, "Pasteur's work on attenuation of virus," and Chapter XI, "History of doctrines of immunity," pp. 241–283, with important references, pp. 235–348, with biographical notices of some of the early workers in bacteriology, makes this source the finest concerning the history of immunology.

1223. **Ford, W. W.** 1939. Bacteriology. Paul B. Hoeber, Inc., New York. Chapter XI, "Development of the subject of immunology," is well written and is an excellent source for the history of this speciallized field.

1224. **Morton, L. T.** 1954. Garrison and Morton's medical bibliography. An annotated check-list of texts illustrating the history of medicine. 2d ed. Printed by W. J.

Rawlinson, Ltd., Netherlands. See section, infection; immunology; serology, pp. 221–225; and allergy and anaphylaxis, pp. 226–228. An annotated bibliography of the development of immunology. One of the finest sources for historical development.

In addition, the following have some historical value:

1225. **Bogomolets, A. A.** 1946. The prolongation of life. A Robinson Foundation Publication. Essential Books. 98 pp. Transl. by Karpovich, P. V., and Bleeker, S. Duell, Sloan & Pearce, New York. This describes his production of antireticular cytotoxic serum (ACS).

1226. **Bordet, J.** 1909. Studies in immunity. Trans. by Gay, F. P., John Wiley & Sons, Inc., New York

1227. **Boyd, W. C.** 1956. Fundamentals of immunology. 3d ed. Interscience Publications, Inc., New York. 776 pp. This is an excellent source for references both early and contemporary.

1228. **Brocq-Rousseu, D., and Roussel, G.** 1939. Le serum normal. Proprietes physiologiques. Masson et Cie, Paris. 630 pp. A valuable bibliography of 4,000 titles.

1229. **Burger, M.** 1950. Bacterial polysaccharides. C. C Thomas, Publishers, Springfield, Ill. 272 pp. A very short historical development, pp. 1–3.

1230. **Cameron, G. R.** 1952. Pathology of the cell. Oliver & Boyd, London. A historical survey concerning the relationship of tissue cells to microorganisms, pp. 175–212.

1231. **Collet, A. B.** 1886. M. Pasteur. La Rage le vaccin charbonneux. Bernard Tegnal, Paris. 140 pp.

1232. **Ehrlich, P.** 1906. Collected studies on immunity. John Wiley & Sons, Inc., New York. A remarkable classic.

1233. **Immunity,** 1930. A system of bacteriology in relation to medicine. Vol. VI. Medical Research Council, H. M. S. O., London. 538 pp. Excellent historical sections and references by various authors.

1234. **Kahn, R. L.** 1948. Historical notes on the serology of syphilis. Victor Robinson Memorial Vol., pp. 157–161. Froben Press, New York.

1235. **Landsteiner, K.** 1945. The specificity of serological reactions. Harvard Univ. Press, Cambridge. 310 pp.

Excellent coverage of the literature. Note listings of textbooks, reviews, monographs, and surveys, pp. 295–297.

1236. **Metchnikoff, E.** 1905. Immunity in infective diseases. Harvard Univ. Press, Cambridge. 591 pp. One of the classics.

1237. **Neuburger, M.** 1932. Forerunners of serum therapy. Medical Life, 39, 707–710.

1238. **Nuttall, G. H. F.** 1904. Blood immunity and blood relationship. Harvard Univ. Press, Cambridge. One of the early classics.

1239. **von Pirquet, C. F.,** and **Schick, B.** (1905). Transl., 1951, by Schick, B. Serum sickness. Williams & Wilkins Co., Baltimore. 130 pp. The first treatise on allergy.

1240. **Ramon, G.** 1950. Le principe des anatoxines et ses applications. Travaux d'Immunologie. Masson et Cie, Paris. 231 pp. Ramon reports in this book on his discovery of anatoxins and on the results obtained from their application in different countries. Lists Ramon's 622 scientific papers. Most immunologists will not agree with Ramon's attempts to disprove Ehrlich's views on toxin and toxoids.

1241. **Reynes, L.** 1939. Étude bibliographique sur l'origine des anticorps. Lyons. Seventy-five entries.

1242. **Richet, C.** 1932. Les origines de la serotherapie; son passé, son present, son avenir. Bull. de l'Acad. de médecine, 108, 1164–1169.

1243. **Rosenthal, S. R.** 1957. BCG vaccination against tuberculosis, with sections by Guérin, C., Weill-Hallé, B., and Wallgren, A. Little, Brown & Co., Boston. 389 pp. An excellent account of the history of BCG by Dr. Camille Guérin, pp. 48–57, with references.

1244. **Schwartzman, G.** 1937. Phenomenon of local tissue reactivity and its immunological, pathological and clinical significance. Foreword by Bordet, J. Paul B. Hoeber, Inc., New York. A selected bibliography is given. This monograph presents a report of extensive experimental work carried out by the author after his discovery, in September, 1927, of the phenomenon of local skin reactivity to bacterial filtrates.

1245. **Symposium.** 1956. Venoms. Ed. by Buckley, E. E., and Porges, N. Publ. No. 44. A. A. A. Sci., Washington,

D. C. 467 pp. Short historical introduction, pp. 1–4.
Excellent list of references following each section.

1246. **Symposium.** 1951. History of allergy. Ciba Symposia,
      11, 1382–1412. Very well done.

1247. **Taliaferra, W. H.** 1929. The immunology of parasitic in-
      fection. The Century Co., New York. A classical
      account.

1248. **Thompson, D.,** and **Thomson, R.** 1948. Oral vaccines.
      The Pickett-Thomson Res. Lab., London. E. & S.
      Livingstone, Ltd., Edinburgh. Short historical section,
      pp. 1–3. References, pp. 291–312.

The following annotated bibliographies are of value:

1249. **Baer, K. A.** 1951. Plasma substitutes (except those de-
      rived from human blood). Army Med. Library, Washing-
      ton, D. C. 141 pp.

1250. **Ginger, L. G., Windle, W. F.,** and **Johnson, I. E.** (eds.).
      1952. Bacterial pyrogens (particularly pyrogenic poly-
      saccharides of bacterial origin): an annotated bibli-
      ography. Baxter Laboratories, Morton Grove, Ill. Covers
      period from 1785 to August, 1952. 377 pp.

Also see section on **Toxins.**

55

INDUSTRIAL

1260. **Bulloch, W.** 1930. The history of bacteriology. *In* A sys-
      tem of bacteriology. Medical Research Council,
      H. M. S. O., London. Vol. 1. Section "Fermentation,"
      pp. 23–28, with excellent listing of references, such as
      the work of Appert (1810), Berzelius (1836), Buchner
      (1903), Leeuwenhoek (1680), Liebig (1939), Pasteur
      (numerous references), Schwann (1837), Traube (1858),
      Wöhler (1901), and others.

1261. _____. 1938. The history of bacteriology. Oxford
      Univ. Press, London. Section on "Fermentation,"

pp. 41–63. List of references, pp. 290–294, more extensive than his first publication, listed above, in 1930.

1262. **Ford, W. W.** 1939. Bacteriology. Paul B. Hoeber, Inc., New York. A good source but not as extensive as Bulloch's.

The more modern development of fermentation may be found in the following two excellent publications:

1263. **Delbrück, M.** 1925. Illustriertes Brauerei-Lexikon, 2. Aufl. hrsg. v. Hayduck, F. Berlin. 3 vols.

1264. **Harden, A.** 1911. Alcoholic fermentation. Longmans, Green & Co., London. Excellent monograph with a valuable bibliography. 3d ed., 1923.

In addition, the following have specific interests:

1265. **Foster, J. W.** 1949. Chemical activities of fungi. Academic Press, Inc., New York. 648 pp.

1266. **Gershenfeld, L.** 1939. Biological products. Romaine Pierson, Publishers, New York. 244 pp. An extensive bibliography that would be an aid for a basis of a historical investigation.

1267. **Greathouse, G. A.,** and **Wessel, C. H.** (eds.). 1954. Deterioration of materials. Causes and preventive techniques. Reinhold Publishing Corp., New York. 835 pp. A symposium with bibliographies at the ends of the chapters. The chapter, "Biological agents of deterioration" of direct interest to the bacteriologist.

1268. **Jørgensen, H.** 1948. Centenary of a microbiologist. A 60-year-old textbook (Microorganisms and fermentation, by the late Alfred Jørgensen, rewritten by Hansen, A., still in use). Danish Foreign Office J. Nr. 4, 21–24. A classic textbook.

1269. **Owen, W. L.** 1949. The microbiology of sugars, syrups and molasses. A reference book for the raw sugar manufacturer or refiner and for all industries engaged in the manufacture, storage or commercial utilization of sugars, syrups and molasses. Barr-Owen Research Enterprises, Baton Rouge, La. Printed by Burgess, Minneapolis. 275 pp. The author has tried to provide a historical review, as indicated by the bibliography.

1270. **Prescott, S. C.,** and **Dunn, C. G.** 1949. Industrial microbiology. 2d ed. McGraw-Hill Book Co., Inc., New York.

923 pp. An excellent listing of references follows each
chapter. A fine source for historical studies.

1271. **Sanford, M.** 1943. Historical development of microbiological methods in vitamin research. Nature, 152, 374–376.

1272. **Siler, J. F.** *et al.* 1941. Immunization to typhoid fever.
The Johns Hopkins Press, Baltimore. 276 pp. This is
one of the classics that includes the techniques for the
manufacture of this vaccine for typhoid fever.

1273. **Siu, R. G.** 1951. Microbial decomposition of cellulose.
With special reference to cotton textiles. Reinhold Publishing Corp., New York. 531 pp. An extremely comprehensive review of significant contribution to this
literature.

1274. **Smith, G.** 1942. An introduction to industrial mycology.
2d ed. Foreword by Raistrick, H. Longmans, Green &
Co., New York. The chief value of this book from the
historical point is the useful listings of books, journals,
and other sources devoted to industrial mycology.

1275. **Smith, J.** 1941. Technical literature of the fermentation
industries. Wallerstein Lab. Comm., 4, 172–175.

1276. **Tauber, H.** 1949. The chemistry and technology of enzymes. John Wiley & Sons, Inc., New York. 550 pp.
Useful listing of references.

1277. **Thaysen, A. C.**, and **Bunker, H. J.** 1927. The microbiology of cellulose, hemicelluloses, pectin and gums.
Oxford University Press, London. One of the early
classics.

56

INSECT

1288. **Steinhaus, E. A.** 1940. The microbiology of insects. With
special reference to the biologic relationships between
bacteria and insects. Bact. Revs., 4, 17–57. An excellent historical background with 203 references.

1289. _____. 1942. Catalogue of bacteria associated
extracellularly with insects and ticks. Burgess Publishing Co., Minneapolis, Minn. 206 pp. Short descriptions and excellent list of references. Many bacterial
names not found in Bergey's Manual.

1290. _____. 1946. Insect microbiology. An account
of the microbes associated with insets and ticks, with
special reference to the biologic relationships involved.
Comstock Publishing Co., Ithaca, N. Y. 763 pp. A
short section on history, pp. 3–8. The outstanding
publication in this field. An extensive bibliography,
pp. 603–691.

1291. _____. 1949. Principles of insect pathology.
McGraw-Hill Book Co., Inc., New York. Brief section
on historical background. Extensive references at the
ends of chapters of some interest to the bacteriologist.

1292. _____. 1949. Nomenclature and classification
of insect viruses. Bact. Revs., 13, 203–223.

1293. _____. 1956. Microbial control—the emergence
of an idea. Hilgardia, 26, 107–160. Insect microbiology
has influenced the development and progress of microbiology. A brief history of insect pathology through the
nineteenth century. Worthy of careful perusal. Excellent
bibliography, pp. 148–157.

1294. _____. 1957. Microbial diseases of insects.
Ann. Rev. Microbiol., 11, 165–182.

57

MARINE

1304. **Lillie, F. R.** 1944. The Woods Hole marine biological
laboratory. Univ. of Chicago Press. 284 pp. Excellent
source material.

1305. **ZoBell, C. E.** 1946. Marine microbiology. Foreword by
Waksman, S. A. Chronica Botanica Co., Waltham, Mass.
240 pp. An outstanding publication. Short history,
pp. 1–9. Extensive bibliography, pp. 209–230.

Comprehensive reviews:

1306. **Beneche, W.** 1933. Abderhalden's Handb. biol. Arbeits-
methoden. Abt. IX, 5, 717–854.

1307. **Wood, E. J. F.** 1958. The significance of marine microbiology. Bact. Revs., 22, 1–19.

1308. **ZoBell, C. E.** 1947. Marine bacteriology. Ann. Rev.
Biochem., 16, 565–586.

58

MATHEMATICS

There is no publication concerning this history, but the following two publications are listed, for they are believed to be the first of their kind, at least in the English language:

1318. **Halvorson, H. O., and Ziegler, N. R.** 1933. Quantitative bacteriology. The Burgess Publishing Co., Minneapolis, Minn. 64 pp. Sampling problems.
1319. **Rahn, O.** 1939. Mathematics in bacteriology. The Burgess Publishing Co., Minneapolis, Minn. 63 pp.

The following three contemporary reviews are of some significance in historical studies:

1320. **Eisenhart, C., and Wilson, P. W.** 1942. Statistical methods and control in bacteriology. Bact. Revs., 7, 57–137. One hundred twenty-five references.
1321. **Stearman, R. L.** 1955. Statistical concepts in microbiology. Bact. Revs., 19, 160–215. An excellent paper with 37 references.
1322. **Thompson, W. R.** 1947. Use of moving averages and interpolation to estimate median-effective dose. I. Fundamental formulas, estimation of error, and relation to other methods. Bact. Revs., 11, 115–145. Forty-nine references

In addition one should consult the history of statistics. The following reference is an excellent source:

1323. **Sarton, G.** 1952. Horus. A guide to the history of science. A Chronica Botanica Publication. The Ronald Press Co., New York. History of statistics, pp. 155–156. A listing of the important historical references.

59

MEDICAL

An outstanding guide to the history of medicine which may be of value to the medical bacteriologist is:

1333. **Morton, L. T.** 1954. Garrison and Morton's medical bibli-
       ography. An annotated check-list of texts illustrating
       the history of medicine. 2d ed. Printed by W. J.
       Rawlinson, Ltd., Netherlands. 655 pp. This is the
       most useful reference work in this area and contains
       6,808 annotated entries. Several of the more useful
       sections for the bacteriologist are listed here:

       History of medicine, pp. 558–574. (Histories of
       special subjects are found under those subjects.)
       Allergy and anaphylaxis, pp. 226–228.
       Antibiotics, pp. 168–170.

       Bacteriology, pp. 215–220. A very useful listing in
       chronological order. This is a remarkable check list
       for the medical bacteriologist.

       Biology, subdivisions, such as: evolution, heredity,
       genetics, microscopy, pp. 10–24.

       Communicable diseases, subdivided, such as: enteric
       fever, diphtheria, scarlet fever, whooping cough, etc.,
       pp. 438–486. This is the finest single source that has
       been published.

       Epidemiology, pp. 146–147.
       Infection, immunology, serology, pp. 221–225.
       Medical biography, pp. 581–584.
       State medicine; public health, hygiene, pp. 140–146.
       Sulphonamides, pp. 170–171.
       Periodicals devoted to the history of medicine, pp.
       578–581.

60

MICROPALAEONTOLOGY

1343. **Glaessner, M. F.** 1948. Principles of micropalaeontology.
       2d ed. John Wiley & Sons, Inc., New York. 296 pp. In-
       cludes bacteria. Excellent bibliography. The first sec-
       tion contains a historical summary of this field.

61

MICROSCOPE

LIGHT

Note excellent reviews in various issues of Isis, under Critical Bibliography, e.g., Eighty-first Critical Bibliography. 1956. Isis, 47, 273. (Section b. Microscopes and microbiology under H. S. 24, Biological Sciences.) Also see Bulloch's book.

1353. **Allen, R. M.** 1940. The microscope. D. Van Nostrand Co., Inc., New York. 286 pp. A chapter on the history of the microscope. See review in Nature, 147, 129 (1941).

1354. **Anon.** 1948. The evolution of the microscope. 3d ed. Amer. Opt., Buffalo, N. Y. A short history.

1355. **Auerbach, F.** 1927. The Zeiss works and the Carl Zeiss foundation in Jena: their scientific, technical, and sociological development, and importance popularly described. Transl. from the fifth German edition by Kanthack, R. W. and G. Foyle, London. 273 pp.

1356. ***Bunyan, J.** 1957. The history of the microscope. To be published. Blackwell's, England. Includes short biographies of the great microscopists and microscope makers.

1357. **Carpenter, W. B.** 1856. The microscope and its revelations. Blanchard & Lea, Philadelphia. One of the classics in this field. Many additional editions.

1358. **Catalogue of the Books in the Library of the Quekett Microscopical Club.** 1904. 72 pp. (1500 ref.)

1359. **Clarke, B. E.** 1942. The history of the microscope and early microscopy. Rhode I. Med. J., 25, 131–139.

1360. **Clay, R. S., and Court, T. H.** 1932. The history of the microscope. Charles Griffin & Co., Ltd., London. 266 pp. A detailed history through early nineteenth century. Listing instrument makers. Illustrations. See review by Kofoid, C. A. 1934. Isis, 21, 227–230.

1361. **Cole, F. J.** 1938. Microscopic science in Holland in the seventeenth century. Jour. Quekett microscopical club, 1. 20 pp. Leeuwenhoek, Swammerdam, Ruysch.

1362. **Disney, A. N., Hill, C. F., and Baker, W. E. W.** 1928. Origin and development of the microscope. The Royal Microscopical Society, London. 303 pp. See review in Isis, **20**, 495–497 (1933).

1363. **Fassin, G.** 1934. Something about the early history of the microscope. Sc. Monthly, **38**, 452–459.

1364. **Ford, W. W.** 1934. Development of our early knowledge concerning magnification. Science, **79**, 578–581.

1365. **Frison, E.** 1951. Historical survey of the use of divergent and correcting lenses in the microscope. The Microscopist, **8**, 115–120.

1366. _____. 1954. L'evolution de la partie optique du microscope au cours du dix-neuvieme siecle. Les test objects, les Test-, Probe-, et Typen-Platten. (=Communications No. 89 du Rijksmuseum voor de Geschiedenis der Natuurweteuschappen.) Musée National d'Histoire des Sciences Exactes et Naturelles, Leyden. 168 pp. See review by Klemn, F. 1955. Sudhoffs Arch., **39**, 189. van Cittert, P. H. 1954. Arch. int. Hist. Sci., **33**, 364–365.

1367. **Gage, S. H.** 1941. The microscope. 17th ed. Comstock Publishing Co., Ithaca, N. Y. 1st ed., 1892. History of lenses and microscopes. A classic with a bibliography of 15 pp.

1368. **Genung, E. F.** 1942. The development of the compound microscope. Bul. Hist. Med., **12**, 575–594.

1369. **Haden, R. L.** 1939. The origin of the microscope. Annals Med. Hist. **1**, 30–44.

1370. **Harting, P.** 1848–54. Het mikroskoop. 4 vols. Utrecht. Exhaustive history. Transl. into German in 2d ed., 1866.

1371. **Lewis, F. T.** 1943. The advent of microscopes in America. Sci. Monthly, **57**, 249–259.

1372. **Morton, L. T.** 1954. Garrison and Morton's medical bibliography. An annotated check-list of texts illustrating the history of medicine. 2d ed. W. J. Rawlinson, Ltd., Netherlands. See section, microscopy, pp. 24–25, for excellent listing of important historical references.

1373. **Muñoz, F. J.**, in collaboration with Charipper, H. A. 1943. The microscope and its use. Chemical Publishing Co., New York. Introductory chapter on the evolution of the microscope.

1374. Nachet, A. 1929. Collection Nachet. Instruments scientifiques et livres anciens. Notice sur l'invention du microscope et son évolution. Liste de savants, constructeurs and amateurs du XVIe siecle. Petit, Paris. Excellent information about European contributions. Illustrated catalog.

1375. Roper, F. C. S. 1865. Catalogue of works on the microscope, and of those referring to microscopical subjects, in the library of Freeman C. S. Roper. Pp. vii, 5–102 (1000 items). Privately printed.

1376. Royal Microscopical Society. 1928. Origin and development of the microscope, as illustrated by catalogues of the instruments and accessories, in the collections of the ... together with bibliographies of original authorities ... Ed. by Disney, A. N., in collaboration with Hill, C. F., and Baker, W. E. W. Preceded by a historical survey on the early progress of optical science. The Society, London. 303 pp. Excellent historical account. Useful bibliography. One of the best sources about early history of optics. Descriptions of microscopes.

1377. Séguy, E. 1942. Le microscope: Emploi et applications. Vol. I. Encylopédié Pratique du Naturaliste, 33. Paul Lechevalier, Paris. Intended for the amateur microscopist. Short section on the history of microscopy.

1378. Singer, C. 1914. Notes on the early history of microscopy. Proc. Roy. Soc. Med., 7 (Sect. Hist. Med.), 247–279.

1379. ———. 1915. The dawn of microscopical discovery. J. Roy. Microsc. Soc., pp. 317–340.

1380. ———. 1921. Steps leading to the invention of the first optical apparatus. Studies in the history of science. Vol. II, pp. 385–413, 533–534. Oxford.

1381. ———. 1953. The earliest figures of microscopic objects. Endeavor, 12, 197–201.

1382. Three American Microscope Builders. 1945. American Optical Co., Buffalo, N. Y.

1383. Turrière, E. 1925. Introduction à l'histoire de l'Optique. Isis, 7, 77–104.

1384. Woodruff, L. L. 1939. Microscopy before the nineteenth century. American Naturalist, 73, 485–516.

1385. ———. 1939. Some pioneers in microscopy, with special reference to protozoölogy. Trans. N. Y. Acad. Sci., 1, 74–77.

1386. _____. 1943. The advent of the microscope at
      Yale College. Am. Scientist, 31, 241-245.
1387. **Wredden, J. H.** 1947. The microscope: its theory and
      applications. With an historical introduction by Watson-
      Baker, W. E. Churchill, London.

      See also listing of articles in:

1388. **Index-Catalogue of the Library of the Surgeon General's
      Office,** United States Army (Armed Forces Medical
      Library). 1955. Vol. 11. U. S. Government Printing
      Office, Washington D. C. P. 92 (History).

ELECTRON

1398. **Bibliography of Electron Microscopy.** 1950–date. On
      Keysort cards keyed and punched according to both
      subject and author. N. Y. Soc. Electron Microscopists,
      New York.
1399. **Cosslett, V. E.** 1950. Bibliography of electron micro-
      scopy. Edward Arnold & Co., London. 350 pp.
1400. **The Electron Microscope, Mainly 1939–41.** 1942. Science
      library: Bibliographical series (No. 567). Reproduced
      from typewriting; 35 references.
1401. **Gabor, D.** 1948. The electron microscope. Its develop-
      ment, present performance, and future possibilities.
      Chemical Publishing Co., Brooklyn, N. Y. 164 pp.
      Adequate bibliography.
1402. **Hawley, G. G.** 1945. Seeing the invisible. The story of
      the electron microscope. Alfred A. Knopf, Inc., New
      York. 195 pp. The history of the instrument is re-
      counted.
1403. **Plenk, H.** 1948. Von der Lupe zum Elektronenmikroskop.
      Wien. 67 pp.

      Other useful publications:

1404. **von Ardenne, M.** 1943. Elektronen-Ubermikroskopie,
      Physik-Technik-Ergebnisse. Photo-Lithoprint Repro-
      ductions, Edwards Bros., Inc., Publishers, Ann Arbor,
      Mich. Verlag von Julius Springer, Berlin. 398 pp.
1405. **von Borries, B.** 1949. Die Ubermikroskopie. W. Saenger,
      Berlin. 416 pp.
1406. **Burton, E. F., and Kohl, W. H.** 1946. The electron mi-
      croscope. An introduction to its fundamental principles
      and applications. 2d ed. Reinhold Publishing Corp.,

New York. 325 pp. Extensive bibliography, pp. 299–
318. See listing of books, p. 299.
1407. **Cosslett, V. E.** 1947. The electron microscope. Sigma
Books, London. 128 pp. Excellent introduction.
1408. **Gregoire, C.** 1950. Microscope électronique et recherche
biologique. (Medicine et biologie). Preface by Claude,
A. Masson et Cie, Paris. 172 pp. Selected bibliography.
1409. **Hall, C. E.** 1953. Introduction to electron microscopy.
McGraw-Hill Book Co., Inc., New York.
1410. **Hillier, J.** 1950. Electron microscopy of microorganisms
and viruses. Annual Rev. Microbiol., 4, 1–20. Excellent short historical introduction. Limitations stressed.
1411. **International Congress of Electron Microscopy.** 1953.
Paris. 2 vols.
1412. **Levaditi, C.** 1949. Images électronique en microbiologie.
Bactéries, rickettsia, spirochetes, ultra-virus, bacterio-
phanges. Libraire Maloine, Paris. 160 pp.
1413. **Symposium.** 1954. Applied electron microscopy. Ed.
by Vandermeerssche, G. Rapport Europeés Congrès
Taegepaste Electronenmicroscopie. Centrum Electronenmicroscopie, Ghent, Belgium. 350 pp. Industrial and
medical applications.
1414. **Symposium.** 1955. Physical techniques in biological research. Ed. by Oster, G., and Pollister, A. W. Vol. 1,
Optical techniques. Academic Press, Inc., New York.
The light microscope. Martin, L. C.
Phase and interference microscopy. Osterberg, H.
Electron microscopy. Cosslett, V. E.
1415. **Symposium.** 1957. Electron microscopy. Ed. by
Sjöstrand, F. S., and Rhodin, J. Academic Press, Inc.,
New York. 355 pp. This volume contains 137 papers
presented at the First European Regional conference on
Electron microscopy, Stockholm, September, 1956.
1416. **Wyckoff, W. G.** 1949. Electron microscopy; technique and
applications. Interscience Publishers, New York. 248
pp. Useful bibliography at end of each section.
1417. **Zworykin, V. K., and Hillier, J.** 1946. Colloid chemistry,
6, 118–159. Ed. by Alexander, J. Reinhold Publishing
Corp., New York. Electron microscope.
1418. **Zworykin, V. K., Morton, G. A., Ramberg, E. G., Hillier, J.,
and Vance, A. W.** 1945. Electron optics and the elec-

tron microscope. John Wiley & Sons, Inc., New York.
766 pp. The first important publication of its kind with
an extensive bibliography.

PHASE

1428. **Bennet, A. H.** 1946. Phase microscopy, its development
and utility. Sci. Monthly, 63, 191–193.
1429. **Bennet, A. H., Jupnik, H., Osterberg, H., and Richards,
O. W.** 1951. Phase microscopy. John Wiley & Sons,
Inc., New York.
1430. **Francon, M.** 1954. Le microscope à contraste de phase
et le microscope interferentiel. CNRS, Paris. Symposium, information on the theory and use of phase.
1431. **Richards, O. W.** 1954. Phase microscopy, 1950–1954.
Science, 120, 631–639. 205 references.
1432. ———. 1956. Phase microscopy, 1954–1956.
Science, 124, 810–814. Extensive bibliography.
1433. **Winkel, R.** 1954. Schriftum-Verzeichnis zur Phasen-
kontrast Mikroskopie. G. M. B. H. Göttingen. Bibliography published by the firm of Winkel.
1434. **Zernike, F.** 1955. How I discovered phase contrast.
Science 121, 345–348. A very interesting historical
account indicating, again, the indifference and resistance to a new method.

62

MORPHOLOGY AND CYTOLOGY

1444. **Bulloch, W.** 1938. The history of bacteriology. Oxford
Univ. Press, London. Although there is no special
section on this phase of bacteriology, the material of
historical importance can easily be found.
1445. **Duclax, E.** 1898. Traité de microbiologie. Masson et
Cie, Paris. Vol. 1. Section, "Morphologie et Structure
des Microbes," pp. 56–81, with excellent listing of
references.
1446. **Leeuwenhoek, Antoni van.** The collected letters of Antoni
van Leeuwenhoek. Ed., illustrated and annotated by a

committee of Dutch scientists. Vol. 1, 1938; vol, 2,
1941; vol. 3, 1948; vol. 4, 1952. Swets & Zeitlinger,
Ltd., Amsterdam. In Dutch and English. There are numerous publications on Leeuwenhoek. This is outstanding.

1447. **Meyer, A.** 1912. Die Zelle der Bakterien. Gustav Fischer,
Jena. 285 pp. An important early comprehensive review
on cytology.

1448. **St. John-Brooks, R.,** and **Barnard, J. E.** 1930. Morphology.
In A system of bacteriology in relation to medicine.
Vol. 1. Medical Research Council, H. M. S. O., London.
Pp. 104–117. An excellent historical development with
a suitable list of references. It includes such important
publications (books) as: Enderlein, G. (1925), Fischer,
A. (1903), Gotschlich, E. (1927), Henrici, A. T. (1928),
Löhnis, F. (1921).

1449. **Smith, E. F.** 1905. Bacteria in relation to plant diseases.
Published by Carnegie Institution of Washington, Washington, D. C. Excellent listing of historical references,
pp. 215–221.

There have been tremendous changes in the field of bacterial cytology rather recently and the historian must be
aware of these advances. A few contemporary references
are given here which have value by their contents and
listings of references:

1450. **Bisset, K. A.** 1950. Cytology and life history of bacteria.
Williams & Wilkins Co., Baltimore. 136 pp.

1451. **Dubos, R. J.** 1945. The bacterial cell. Harvard Univ.
Press, Cambridge. 466 pp. Section on "Cytology of
bacteria," pp. 18–52. Excellent bibliography. An addition by Robinow, C. F. Nuclear apparatus and cell
structure of rod-shaped bacteria, pp. 353–377. This is
an excellent survey of bacterial cytology and its relation
to physiology.

1452. **Knaysi, G.** 1951. Elements of bacterial cytology.
2d ed. Comstock Publishing Co., Ithaca, N. Y. 375 pp.
There is a very short section on the development and
methods of bacterial cytology, pp. 1–3. Excellent bibliography.

1453. **Scanga, F.** 1954. La Cellula Batterica. II Pensiero
Scientifico, Rome, Italy. 477 pp. This publication in-

cludes controversial phases, is richly illustrated, and is probably the most artistically produced volume in this field.

1454. **Winkler, A.** 1956. Die Bakterienzelle. Gustav Fischer Verlag, Stuttgart, Germany. An excellent critical survey of bacterial cytology.

Symposia: The following are listed, for they are all excellent and stimulating. The contemporary aspects, especially in this area, must be related to the older ideas:

1455. **Symposium.** 1949. The nature of the bacterial surface. Ed. by Miles, A. A., and Pirie, N. W. C. C Thomas, Springfield, Ill. 179 pp.

1456. **Symposium.** 1952. The biology of bacterial spores. Bact. Revs., 16, 89–143.

1457. **Symposium.** 1953. Bacterial cytology. Vol. 1. Symposia of the VIth International Congress of Microbiology. C. C Thomas, Springfield, Ill. 181 pp. Vol. V. Actinomycetales (Morphology, Biology and Systematics). 221 pp.

1458. **Symposium.** 1955. Bacterial anatomy. Sixth symposium of the Society for General Microbiology. Harvard Univ. Press, Cambridge. 360 pp. This is an outstanding attempt to present the controversial material in this field.

In addition, the following contemporary publications have excellent references to the earlier literature:

1459. **Waksman, S. A.** 1950. Actinomycetes. A Chronica Botanica Publication. The Ronald Press Co., New York. 235 pp. Morphology and cytology.

1460. **Wilson, G. S.,** and **Miles, A. A.** 1955. Topley and Wilson's principles of bacteriology and immunity. Williams & Wilkins Co., Baltimore. Vol. 1, Chapter 2, "The biological characteristics of bacteria: morphology," pp. 16–48. A critical review with historical development. Excellent listing of references.

There are numerous reviews. The following are noteworthy:

1461. **Knaysi, G.** 1956. Cytology of bacteria. Ann. Rev. Mictobiol., 10, 253–274.

1462. **Lewis, I. M.** 1941. The cytology of bacteria. Bact. Revs., 5, 181–230. This was the first important classical review of contemporary times.
1463. **Pijper, A.** 1957. Bacterial flagella and motility. Ergebnisse der Mikrobiologie Immunitätsforschung und Experimentellen Therapie. Pp. 39–95. Springer-Verlag, Berlin. Excellent review with historical background. 344 references.
1464. **Tomcsik, J.** 1956. Antibodies as indicators for bacterial structures. Ann. Rev. Microbiol., 10, 213–236.

In reference to the subject of chromatin bodies of bacteria, the following publications are outstanding:

1465. **Delaporte, B.** 1939–1940. Recherches cytologiques sur les bactéries et les cyanophycées. Rev. Gen. Botan., 51, 615–643, 689–708, 748–768; 52, 112–160. Also published as a thesis, Paris, Imprimerie André Lesot, 1–160. The literature on bacterial nuclei from the beginnings of bacteriology to 1939 is presented in this excellent paper.
1466. **Robinow, C. F.** 1957. The chromatin bodies of bacteria. Bact. Revs., 20, 207–242. This paper is remarkable for its historical presentations and excellent critical review. It lists 127 selective papers, including the important work of DeLamater, Bisset, and others.

63

PALEOPATHOLOGY

1476. **Moodie, R. L.** 1923. Paleopathology, an introduction to the study of ancient evidences of disease. Univ. of Illinois Press. A bibliography that includes most publications on the subject up to 1922. See pp. 545–557.
1477. **Pales, L.** 1939. Paléopathologie et pathologie comparative. Masson et Cie, Paris. Contains a bibliography of 660 titles, including those of Moodie's book and additional items from 1923 to 1930.

1478. **Sigerist, H. E.** 1951. A history of medicine. Oxford Univ. Press, London. Note excellent bibliography on paleopathology since 1930, pp. 532-541. The use of x-rays and the application of serological methods have added impetus to these studies.

64

PATHOLOGY

1488. ***Goldschmid, E.** 1925. Entwicklung und Bibliographie der pathologisch—anatomischen Abbildung. K. W. Hiersemann, Leipzig.
1489. **Krumbhaar, E. B.** 1937. Pathology. (Clio Medica). Paul B. Hoeber, Inc., New York.
1490. **Long, E. R.** 1928. A history of pathology. Williams & Wilkins Co., Baltimore. 315 pp.
1491. ———. 1929. Selected readings in pathology. C. C Thomas, Springfield, Ill.
1492. ***Ribbert, H.** 1899. Die Lehre von Wesender Krankheit in ihrer geschichtlichen Entwicklung. Bonn.

In addition, see listings by:

1493. **Morton, L. T.** 1954. Garrison and Morton's medical bibliography. 2d ed. Argosy Bookstore, New York. Pp. 202-203. Lists history of pathology by Chiari, Ruffer, and Moodie.

64

PETROLEUM

1503. **Beerstecher, E.** 1954. Petroleum microbiology. Elservier Press, Inc., New York. 375 pp. Chapter 1, "Introduction," has an excellent historical development, pp. 1–18. Important references are listed at the end of each section. A brief chronology of petroleum microbiology listed on p. 17. A very stimulating and interesting book that covers the literature.

A review of importance concerning contemporary work:

1504. Davis, J. B., and Updegraff, D. M. 1954. Microbiology in the petroleum industry. Bact. Revs., 18, 215–238.

66

PHYSIOLOGY

A history of this area of bacteriology has not been written. It has become difficult to know what to leave out of this section, for bacterial physiology is so varied and extensive.

1514. Barker, H. A. 1956. Bacterial fermentations. John Wiley & Sons, Inc., New York. 95 pp. Excellent historical introduction.

1515. Buchanan, R. E., and Fulmer, E. I. 1928. Physiology and biochemistry of bacteria. 3 vols. Williams & Wilkins Co., Baltimore. Vol. 1, 516 pp.; Vol. II, 709 pp.; Vol. III, 575 pp. This is the early classic. A tremendous coverage of the enormous earlier literature.

1516. Harvey, E. N. 1957. A history of luminescence. From the earliest times until 1900. The Amer. Philos. Soc., Philadelphia. 692 pp. Use index for reference to bacteria.

1517. Hewitt, L. F. 1950. Oxidation-reduction potentials in bacteriology and biochemistry. 6th ed. Livingstone, Edinburgh. Valuable references.

1518. Jordan, E. O., and Falk, I. S. (eds.). 1928. The newer knowledge of bacteriology and immunology. The Univ. of Chicago Press. 1196 pp. Several articles dealing with bacterial physiology that have some historical references.

1519. **Knight, B. C. J. G.** 1945. Growth factors in microbiology. Some wider aspects of nutritional studies with micro-organisms. Vitamins and Hormones, 3, 108–228. Excellent short historical development of the study of the nutrition of microorganisms. (460 ref.)

1520. **McLeod, J. W.** 1930. Bacterial respiration. *In* A system of bacteriology in relation to medicine. Vol. 1. Medical Research Council, H. M. S. O., London. Pp. 228–291. Historical material scattered in this publication.

1521. **van Niel, C. B.** 1944. Recent advances in our knowledge of the physiology of microorganisms. Bact. Revs., 8, 225–234.

1522. **Oginsky, E. L., and Umbreit, W. W.** 1954. An introduction to bacteria physiology. W. H. Freeman & Co., San Francisco, Calif. 404 pp. This book does not deal with historical development, although it is stimulating and provocative. It is recommended because of its fine listing of the more important publications in this field with excellent short annotations. Mostly English publications.

1523. **Porter, J. R.** 1946. Bacterial chemistry and physiology. John Wiley & Sons, Inc., New York. This book covers the gap from Buchanan and Fulmer's publication. Tremendous coverage of the literature, with references at the ends of chapters.

1524. **Stephenson, M.** 1949. Bacterial metabolism. 3d ed. Longmans, Green & Co., London. 398 pp. An excellent bibliography, pp. 321–382. This is the only publication of a vast number in bacterial physiology that makes an attempt to discuss its history. Short history, pp. 1–11.

1525. **Twort, F. W., and Ingram, C. L. Y.** 1913. A monograph on Johne's disease. Baillière, Tindall & Cox, London. This is one of the very few classics in the history of bacterial chemistry. One of the earliest studies in the field of bacterial growth factors.

1526. **Wilson, G. S., and Miles, A. A.** 1955. Topley and Wilson's principles of bacteriology and immunity. 4th ed. Williams & Wilkins Co., Baltimore. 2 vols. 2,331 pp. This publication is the outstanding one in the medical field and covers the literature well.

1527. **Wilson, P. W.** 1953. The early and somewhat diverting history of the division of physiology, Society of American Bacteriologists. News Letter, Soc. Amer. Bacteriologists, 19, 2-3.

See sections on specific bacteria, Chemical Composition; Cultivation and Identification; Growth and Death; Industrial; Chemical Agents—Harmful Effect on Bacteria; Physical Agents—Harmful Effect on Bacteria; Insect; Marine; Petroleum; etc.

67

PHYSICAL AGENTS—HARMFUL EFFECT ON BACTERIA

1536. **Buchanan, R. E., and Fulmer, E. I.** 1930. Physiology and biochemistry of bacteria. 3 vols. Williams & Wilkins Co., Baltimore.

1537. **Hampil, B.** 1932. The influence of temperature on the life processes and death of bacteria. Quart. Rev. Biol. 7, 172-196. An excellent historical review with references.

1538. **Lautenschläger, L., and Schmidt, H.** 1954. Sterilisations-Methoden für die Pharmazeutische und Arztliche Praxis. Georg Thieme Verlag, Stuttgart. 320 pp. Short introduction and history, pp. 1-6. An excellent listing for historical studies in Anhang II, pp. 286-314.

1539. **Lea, D. E.** 1947. Actions of radiations on living cells. The Macmillan Co., New York. 402 pp. Sections on bacteria and viruses with references.

1540. **Magath, T. B.** 1937. The history of steam sterilization. Annals Med. Hist., 9, 338-344.

1541. **Perkins, J. J.** 1956. Principles and methods of sterilization. C. C Thomas, Springfield, Ill. 340 pp. An excellent chapter, "Historical introduction," pp. 3-32, with a list of 43 important historical references.

1542. **Porter, J. R.** 1946. Bacterial chemistry and physiology. John Wiley & Sons, Inc., New York. A section on "The effects of physical agents on bacteria," pp. 144-223,

with an excellent listing of references fills in the gap
from Buchanan and Fulmer's publication.

1543. **Rahn, O.** 1945. Physical methods of sterilization of
microorganisms. Bact. Revs., 9, 1–47. An excellent
review with historical material. One hundred fifty-four
references.

1544. **Underwood, W. B.** 1946. The story of sterilization. Surgical Supervisor, 6, 3–61.

68

PLANT DISEASES

1554. **Bibliographie der Pflanzenschutzliteratur.** Heraus-
gegeben von der Biologischen Zentralanstalt für Land-
und Forstwirtschaft in Berlin-Dahlem. 1953. Berlin.
First volume in 1921. World list of books and articles
dealing with plant diseases, insects, and pests.

1555. **Chester, K. S.** 1946. The nature and prevention of the
cereal rusts as exemplified in the leaf rust of wheat.
A Chronica Botanica Publication. The Ronald Press
Co., New York. Covers the history of the rusts and an
extensive bibliography is of value.

1556. **Dowson, W. J.** 1957. Plant diseases due to bacteria.
2d ed. At the University Press, Cambridge. 232 pp.

1557. **Elliott, C.** 1951. Manual of bacterial plant pathogens.
A Chronica Botanica Publication. The Ronald Press
Co., New York. 186 pp.

1558. **Garrett, S. D.** 1944. Root disease fungi. A treatise on
the epidemiology of soil-borne disease in crop plants
and a first exposition of the principles of root disease
control. Annales Cryptogamici et Phytopathologici.
Vol. 1. The Chronica Botanica Co., Waltham, Mass.
Introduction covers the historical background of the
subject. A bibliography comprises nearly 450 titles
from the early classics of 1878.

1559. **Gäumann, E.** 1946. Pflanzliche Infektionslehre.
Lehrbuch der Allgemeiner Pflanzenpathologie für

biologen, Landwirte, Förster und Pflanzenzüchter.
Lehrbücher und Monographien aus dem Gebiete der
exakten Wissenschaften, 3. Reihe der experimentellen
Biologie, Band I. Verlag Birkhäuser, Basel. 611 pp.
Monograph on plant diseases. A bibliography of over
600 titles. English translation, 1950, Hafner Publishing
Co., New York.

1560. Heald, F. D. 1933. Manual of plant diseases. 2d ed.
McGraw-Hill Book Co., Inc., New York. Introduction
and history, pp. 1–20. List of important textbooks and
manuals relating to plant diseases, English, German,
and French, pp. 20–25.

1561. Kelman, A. 1953. The bacterial wilt caused by
Pseudomonas solanacearum. A literature review and
bibliography. Tech. Bul. No. 99. Agricultural Experi-
ment Station, North Carolina State College. Extensive
world-wide coverage of the literature.

1562. Klein, R. M., and Link, G. K. K. 1955. The etiology of
crowngall. Quart. Rev. Biol., 30, 207–277. A review
dedicated to the memory of Dr. Erwin Frink Smith (1854–
1927). An extensive review with almost 500 references.
Historical material.

1563. Reed, H. S. 1942. A short history of the plant sciences.
A Chronica Botanica Publication. The Ronald Press
Co., New York. 320 pp. References at ends of chapters.
Note the preface. Reviewed by Zirkle, C. 1942. Isis,
34, 36. "Startling gaps in the history."

1564. Smith, E. F. 1905. Bacteria in relation to plant diseases.
Carnegie Institution of Washington, Washington, D. C.
Vol. 1, 1905; vol. 2, 1911; and vol. 3, 1914. This is
the famous classic in this field. Note bibliography in
vol. 1., pp. 203–266, and the history and earliest workers
vol. 2., pp. 7–22.

1565. Vavilov, N. I. 1951. The origin, variation, immunity and
breeding of cultivated plants. Trans. from the Russian
by Chester, K. S. Selected writings. A Chronica
Botanica Publication. The Ronald Press Co., New York.
364 pp. See Isis 43 (1952), 157–158, for brief reference
to accomplishments of Nikolai Ivanovich Vavilov (1887–
1942).

1566. Whetzel, H. H. 1918. An outline of the history of phytopathology. W. B. Saunders Co., Philadelphia. 130 pp.
See short review by Sarton, G. 1923. Isis, 5, 461–464.

69

QUARANTINE—HISTORY OF

1576. **Cavins, H. M.** 1943. The national quarantine and sanitary conventions of 1857 to 1860. Bull. Hist. Med., 13, 404–426.

1577. **Enger, J. M.** 1903. The early history of quarantine: origin of sanitary measures directed against yellow fever. Yellow Fever Institute, Bull. No. 12. Treasury Dept. Public Health and Marine-Hospital Service. Government Printing Office, Washington, D. C.

1578. **Gerlitt, J.** 1940. The development of quarantine. Ciba Symp., 2, 566–580.

1579. **Leikind, M. C.** 1940. Quarantine in the United States. The quarantine station at Miami, Florida. Ciba Symposia, 2, 581–582, 583–592.

1580. **Rachford, B. K.** 1950. The story of a quarantine. Jour. Hist. Med., 5, 432–443. (Nassau, Bahama in 1889.)

1581. **Ransom, J. E.** 1938. John Howard on quarantine. Bull. Inst. Hist. Med., 6, 111–116.

1582. **Rosen, G.** 1940. Forerunners of quarantine. Ciba Symp., 2, 563–565.

1583. **McDonald, J. C.** 1951. The history of quarantine in Britain during the 19th century. Bull. Hist. Med., 25, 22–44.

70

RADIATION—EFFECT ON BACTERIA

1593. **Lea, D. E.** 1947. Action of radiations on living cells. The Macmillan Book Co., New York. 402 pp. Note the excellent listing of early references concerned with bacteria. Use index for specific subjects.

1594. **Kimball, R. F.** 1957. Nongenetic effects of radiation on microorganisms. Ann. Rev. Microbiol., 11, 199–220. This contemporary review lists a number of important earlier reviews on this subject, such as Hollaender's

"Radiation Biology," Bacq and Alexander's book, reviews by Sparrow and Forro; Mortimer and Beam, and reports by the National Academy of Sciences and Ciba
Foundation Symposium.

In addition the following bibliographies are of historical
interest:

1595. Effect of Ultra Radio Waves on Bacteria. 1935. Science
library, Bibliographical series. (No. 177.) Single sheet,
13 entries. Second edition. Action of ultra-short radio
waves on bacteria and insects. (No. 257.) Reproduced
from typewriting, 36 entries. Action of high frequency
fields on insects and bacteria. (No. 676.) 1949. 35
entries.

1596. Robinson, R. F., Phillips, M. D., and Nagelsen, M. G.
1951. A bibliography on "The effects of x-rays on
bacteria." 1896–August, 1951. Battelle Memorial Institute, Columbus, Ohio. 178 references.

1597. Stephens, S. V., and Boche, R. D. 1953. Annotated bibliography in radio-biology. U. S. Atomic Energy Commission, Technical Information Service, Oak Ridge, Tenn.
360 pp. Covers material from about 1932–1951.

71

RICKETTSIALES

1607. Holmes, W. H. 1940. Bacillary and rickettsial infections.
The Macmillan Co., New York. 676 pp. Excellent short
historical sections. References at the ends of chapters.
One of the classic examples of the excellent use of his-
torical presentation in a textbook. Highly recommended,
Black death to white plague.

1608. Price, E. G. 1949. Fighting spotted fever in the Rockies.
Naegele Printing Co., Helena, Mont. 269 pp. Bibliography, pp. 248–257. An excellent history of the American
work.

1609. **Zinsser, H.** 1935. Rats, lice and history. Blue Ribbon Books, New York, and Little Brown & Co., Boston. 301 pp. One of the great popular classics dealing with the life history of typhus fever.

The following three symposia are of some historical interest:

1610. **Symposium.** 1940. Virus and rickettsial diseases. Harvard Univ. Press, Cambridge. One of the first symposiums of this nature on these subjects. An article by Wolbach, S. B. "The rickettsial diseases. A general survey," pp. 789–816, of interest.

1611. **Symposium.** 1948. Rickettsial diseases of man. Organized by Soule, M. H. Ed. by Moulton, F. R. Amer. Assoc. Adv. Sci., Washington, D. C.

1612. **Symposium.** 1953. Virus and rickettsial classification and nomenclature. Annals N. Y. Acad. Sciences, 56, 381–622.

Reviews of interest:

1613. **Pinkerton, H.** 1942. The pathogenic rickettsiae with particular reference to their nature, biological properties, and classification. Bact. Revs., 6, 37–78. A historical development with 133 references.

1614. **Weatworth, B. B.** 1955. Historical review of the literature on Q fever. Bact. Revs., 19, 129–149.

72

SAFETY

1624. **Reitman, M.,** and **Wedum, A. G.** 1956. Microbiological safety. Pub. Health Repts., 71, 659–665. Nineteen references.

1625. **Wedum, A. G.** 1953. Bacteriological safety. Amer. Jour. Pub. Health, 43, 1428–1434. References, pp. 1433–1434.

73

SANITARY

1635. **Hanlon, J. J.** 1958. A bookshelf on international health.
Amer. Jour. Pub. Health, 48, 413–424.

An outstanding guide to the important references concerning the history of state medicine, public health, hygiene, epidemiology, communicable diseases, tropical
medicine, etc., is found in:

1636. **Morton, L. T.** 1954. Garrison and Morton's medical bibliography. An annotated check-list of texts illustrating
the history of medicine. 2d ed. Printed by W. J.
Rawlinson, Ltd., Netherlands. 655 pp. The sanitary
bacteriologist will find this a most useful source for the
important historical references.

In addition, the following selective articles and books
may be of value:

1637. **Boyd, M. F.** 1946. Preventive medicine. 7th ed. W. B.
Saunders & Co., Philadelphia. An excellent listing of
periodicals, serials, books, etc., in sanitation, communicable diseases, hygiene, etc., pp. 560–566. Unfortunately only English titles.

1638. **Horwood, M. P.** 1952. Sixty years of progress in sanitation, 1890–1950. Modern Sanitation, New York.

1639. **Kramer, H. D.** 1948. The germ theory and early public
health program in the United States. Bul. Hist. Med.,
22, 233–247.

1640. **Ravenel, M. P.** (ed.). 1921. A half century of public
health. Jubilee historical volume of the American Public
Health Association, New York. Includes, Gorham, F. P.
The history of bacteriology and its contribution to public
health work.

1641. **Reingold, N.** 1955. The national archives and the history
of science in America. Isis, 46, 22–28. "The laboratory
research of the Public Health Service can be traced
back to a one-room bacteriological laboratory established
in 1887 to aid quarantine enforcement."

1642. Sigerist, H. E. 1956. Landmarks in the history of hygiene. Oxford Univ. Press. 78 pp.

1643. Sudhoff, K. 1917. The hygienic idea and its manifestations in world history. Annals Med. Hist., 1, 111–117.

1644. Symposium. 1928. Historic review of the development of sanitary engineering in the United States during the past one-hundred and fifty years. Tr. Am. Soc. Civil Eng., 92.

1645. Symposium. 1953. Century of progress through sanitation. Amer. Jour. Public Health, 43, 7–30. A brief history concerned mainly with progress in America.

1646. U. S. Public Health Service. 1938. A brief history of bacteriological investigations of the United States Public Health Service. Pub. Health Repts., Supp. 141.

1647. Welch, F. B. 1945/46. History of sanitation. Sanitarian, 8, 39–51.

1648. Williams, R. C. 1951. The United States Public Health Service, 1798-1950. Commissioned Officers Assoc. of the United States Public Health Service, Washington, D. C. 890 pp. See review by Hiscock, I. 1952. J. Hist. Med., 7, 428–429.

In addition, one can find numerous selective lists of references to hygiene, sanitation, etc., in a number of publications concerned with the history of medicine. See Morton, L. T.

Also refer to Chemical Agents—Harmful Effects on Bacteria, Dairy, Food, Air, Water, and Sewage and Industrial Wastes.

74

SEWAGE AND INDUSTRIAL WASTES

1658. Morton, L. T. 1954. Garrison and Morton's medical bibliography. An annotated check-list of texts illustrating the history of medicine. 2d ed. Printed by W. J.

Rawlinson, Ltd., Netherlands. Note section, State
medicine: Public Health: Hygiene, pp. 140-146.

The following may also be of use:

1659. **Frankland, E.** 1870. First report of the commission appointed in 1868 to inquire into the best means of pre-
venting the pollution of rivers. London.

1660. **Garrison, F. H.** 1929. The history of drainage, irrigation,
sewage-disposal and water supply. Bul. N. Y. Acad.
Med., 5, 887-928. A brief sketch.

1661. **Hyde, C. G.** 1938. A review of progress in sewage treatment during the past fifty years in the United States.
In Modern sewage disposal. Ed. by Pearse, L. Federation of Sewage Work Assoc., New York.

1662. **Metcalf, L., and Eddy, H. P.** 1935. Development of
sewage treatment and disposal. Pp. 1-17. *In* American
sewerage practice. 3d. ed. Vol. III. McGraw-Hill Book
Co., Inc., New York. 892 pp.

1663. **Mohlman, F. W.** 1929. The role of bacteria in the treatment of sewage. *In* The newer knowledge of bacteriology and immunology. Ed. by Jordan, E. O., and Falk,
I. S. Univ. of Chicago Press. Pp. 351-361. This is one
of the best sources for historical material.

1664. **Rideal, S.** 1901. Sewage and the bacterial purification of
sewage. John Wiley & Sons, Inc., New York. 308 pp.
Introduction and history, pp. 1-20; bacteria occurring in
sewage, pp. 50-74; bacterial purification, history of the
idea and of early experiments, pp. 175-259.

1665. **Southgate, B. A.** 1948. Treatment and disposal of industrial waste waters. H.M.S.O., London. 327 pp. Numerous references at end of chapters valuable for a historical study.

For the medical aspects, consult:

1666. **Wilson, G. S., and Miles, A. A.** 1955. Topley and Wilson's
principles of bacteriology and immunity. 4th ed. The
Williams & Wilkins Co., Baltimore. 2 vols. 2,331 pp.

In addition there are two famous classics in epidemiology that should be noted:

1667. **Budd, W.** 1873. Typhoid fever; its nature, mode of spread-
ing, and prevention. Longmans, Green & Co., London.

Reprinted 1931, Delta Omega Soc., Commonwealth Fund,
New York. 184 pp.

1668. **Snow, J.** 1936. On cholera. Reprint of two papers. The
Commonwealth Fund, New York. 191 pp.

A contemporary publication of interest:

1669. **Belin, V. M.** 1934. Coquillages et fièvres typhoids. Un
point d'histoire contemporaine. Les Presses Universitaires de France, Paris. Contaminated shell-fish con-
sumption in France alone has resulted in approximately
100,000 cases of typhoid fever in a 15-year period.

Handbook:

1670. **Handbook.** 1957. Selected biological references on water
pollution control, sewage treatment, water treatment.
2d ed. U. S. Dept. of Health, Education, and Welfare,
Public Health Service, Washington, D. C. 95 pp.

75

SOIL

1680. **Beijerinck, M. W.** 1921-1946. Verzamelde Geschriften.
6 vols. Delft, Holland. Beijerinck with Winogradsky
were the great workers in this field. Beijerinck is noted
for his great work on physiological specificity of different types and the essential role of microorganisms in
maintaining the cycle of matter. Beijerinck was a
prodigious worker with superb powers of observation and
an insatiable curiosity.

1681. **Ellis, D.** 1919. Iron bacteria. Methuen & Co., London.
A monograph that covers the earlier literature.

1682. _____. 1932. Sulphur bacteria. Longmans, Green & Co.,
New York. A monograph that covers the earlier literature; references, pp. 243-254.

1683. **Large, E. C.** 1940. The advance of the fungi. Henry Holt
& Co., New York. Excellent historical publication with
bibliography, pp. 451-476.

1684. Sternberg, G. M. 1893. A manual of bacteriology. William
        Wood & Co., New York. References to soil, pp. 861-862.
1685. Pochon, J. 1954. Manual technique d'analyse microbiolo-
        gique du sol. Masson et Cie, Paris. A contemporary
        publication of value.
1686. Waksman, S. A. 1927. Principles of soil microbiology.
        Ballière, Tindall & Cox, London. 897 pp. This publi-
        cation has been the giant in the English language writ-
        ten by one of the great soil microbiologists of the world.
        The big three, Beijerinck, Winogradsky, and Waksman.
        A short section on, "History of soil microbiology,"
        pp. 834-843, with important references noted. In the
        front section of the book, Waksman refers to "A classi-
        fied list of books for reference in soil microbiology,"
        pp. xi-xix. This is very valuable for historical studies.
        Such important publications as: Baumgärtel, T. (1925-
        1926), Buchanan, R. E. (1922), Chudiakov, H. H. (1926),
        Duclaux, E. (1898-1901), Fuhrmann, F. (1913), Greaves,
        J. E. (1922), Janke, A. (1924), Kayser, E. (1921),
        Kossowicz, A. (1912), Lafar, F. (1904-1913), Lipman,
        J. G. (1911), Löhnis, F. (1910), Russell, J. (1923),
        Marshall, C. E. (1922), Russell, H. L., and Hastings,
        E. G. (1926), Rossi, G. (1921-1926), Smith, E. F. (1905,
        1911, 1914), Stocklasa, J., and Doerell, E. G. (1926),
        Tanner, F. W. (1919).
1687. _____. 1952. Soil microbiology. John Wiley &
        Sons, Inc., New York. 356 pp. There is an excellent
        short historical account, pp. 1-28. A selected bibli-
        ography lists the important historical publications.
1688. Winogradsky, S. N. 1949. Microbiologie du sol,
        problèmes et méthodes. Cinquante Ans de Recherches.
        Masson et Cie, Paris. 861 pp. A cornerstone in method-
        ology of great importance to bacteriology. The discovery
        of nitrifying bacteria ranks at the top for methodology,
        soundness, reasoning, and originality of thought. Nitro-
        gen fixation.

        There are numerous contemporary reviews that are of
        some historical importance, such as:

1689. Allen, E. K., and Allen, O. N. 1950. Biochemical and
        symbiotic properties of the rhizobia. Bact. Revs., 14,
        273-330.

1690. **Burk, D., and Burris, R. H.** 1914. Biochemical nitrogen
      fixation. Ann. Rev. Biochem., 10, 587–618.
1691. **Cohn, H. J.** 1948. The most abundant groups of bacteria
      in soil. Bact. Revs., 12, 257–273.
1692. **Lockhead, A. G.** 1952. Soil microbiology. Ann. Rev.
      Microbiol., 6, 185–206.
1693. **Smith, N. R.** 1948. Microbiology of soil. Ann. Rev.
      Microbiol., 2, 453–484.
1694. **Thorton, H. G., and Meiklejohn, J.** 1957. Soil Micro-
      biology. Ann. Rev. Microbiol., 11, 123–148.
1695. **Virtanen, A. I.** 1948. Biological nitrogen fixation. Ann.
      Rev. Microbiol., 2, 485–506.
1696. **Wilson, P. W., and Burris, R. H.** 1947. The mechanism of
      biological nitrogen fixation. Bact. Revs., 11, 41–73.
1697. _____. 1953. Biological nitrogen fixation—reappraisal.
      Ann. Rev. Microbiol., 7, 415–432.

76

SPIROCHETES

1707. **Breed, R. S., Murray, E. G. D., and Hitchens, A. P.** 1948.
      Bergey's manual of determinative bacteriology. 6th ed.
      Williams & Wilkins Co., Baltimore. Excellent for the
      listing of the historical references on classification,
      pp. 1051–1079.
1708. **Davis, G. E.** 1948. The spirochetes. Ann. Rev. Micro-
      biol., 2, 305–334. A contemporary review with 131
      references, some of historical importance.
1709. **Geiman, Q. M.** 1952. Metabolism of spirochetes. Ann.
      Rev. Microbiol., 6, 299–316. Eighty-five references.
1710. ***Gsell, O.** 1952. Leptospirosen. Berne.
1711. **Noguchi, H.** 1928. The spirochetes. *In* Newer knowledge
      of bacteriology and immunology. Univ. of Chicago Press.
      Pp. 452–497. One of the classics, with excellent his-
      torical presentation and references.
1712. **Stavitsky, A. B.** 1948. Characteristics of pathogenic
      spirochetes and spirochetoses with special reference to

the mechanism of host resistance. Bact. Revs., 12, 203–255.

1713. **Symposium on the Leptospiroses.** 1953. Army medical service, graduate school, Walter Reed Army Med. Center, Washington, D. C. Government Printing Office, Washington, D. C. 224 pp.

1714. **Wilson, G. S., and Miles, A. A.** 1955. Topley and Wilson's principles of bacteriology and immunity. 4th ed. The Williams & Wilkins Co., Baltimore. Vol. 1., pp. 1031–1056. An excellent source for historical references.

77

SPONTANEOUS GENERATION

1724. **Bulloch, W.** 1930. The history of bacteriology. *In* A system of bacteriology. Medical Research Council, H.M.S.O., London. Vol. 1.

1725. ———. 1938. The history of bacteriology. Oxford Univ. Press, London. Both of these publications have excellent sections on spontaneous generation, with a comprehensive list of references.

1726. **Duclaux, E.** 1898. Traité de microbiologie. Masson et Cie, Paris. Vol. 1, pp. 82–98. Excellent listing of important references, such as: Aristote, Redi (1688), Vallisnieri (1700, 1710), Swammerdam (1737), Leuvenhoeck (1680), Needham (1737, 1768), Buffon, Spallanzani (1787), Schultze (1863), Schwann (1837), Helmholtz (1843), Schröder and van Dusch (1854), Pouchet (1859), Pasteur (1882), Tyndall (1881), and Chamberland.

1727. **Grasset, H.** 1911–1912. Étude historique et critique sur les générations spontanées et l'hétérogénie. France médicale.

1728. **Hofsten, N. von.** 1936. Ideas of creation and spontaneous generation prior to Darwin. Isis, 25, 80–94.

1729. **Lindroth, S.** 1939. La génération spontanée. Lychnos, 159–191. In Swedish, with summary in French, pp. 191–192.

1730. **Symposium.** 1957. Modern ideas on spontaneous generation. Annals N. Y. Acad. Sciences, 69, 255–376. This
is worthy of perusal.

78

STAINING

1740. **Baker, J. R.** 1945. The discovery of the uses of colouring
agents in biological microtechnique. Monograph of
Quekett Microscopical Club. Orig. published in its Jour.,
Ser. 4, Vol. 1, No. 6. Williams & Norgate, London. Interesting historical monograph on the discovery of
biological staining.
1741. **Bartholomew, J. W., and Mittwer, T.** 1952. The Gram
stain. Bact. Revs., 16, 1–29. A short historical introduction with 150 references.
1742. **Bartholomew, J. W., and Umbreit, W. W.** 1944. Ribonucleic
acid and the Gram stain. J. Bact., 48, 567. Detailed
survey of older theories given.
1743. **Bulloch, W.** 1930. History of bacteriology. *In* A system
of bacteriology. Vol. 1. Med. Res. Council, H.M.S.O.,
London. Excellent short section on history of staining,
pp. 68–70.
1744. ———. 1938. The history of bacteriology. Oxford
Univ. Press, London. See excellent section, "Staining
methods for bacteria," pp. 213–217.
1745. **Churchman, J. W.** 1928. Staining reactions of bacteria.
In Newer knowledge of bacteriology and immunology.
Ed. by Jordan, E. O., and Falk, I. S. Univ. of Chicago
Press. Pp. 19–37. Historical material available.
1746. **Conn, H. J.** 1946. Development of histological staining.
Ciba Symposis, 7, 270–300. Chronology, the evolution
of histological staining, the staining of fixed tissues,
vital staining, bibliography.
1747. ———. 1948. The history of staining. 2d ed. Biotechnical Publications, Geneva, N. Y. 141 pp. This is
the outstanding publication of its kind. Bibliography at
the end of each chapter. Section on "The development
of bacteriological staining methods," pp. 75–84, with
references.

1748. _____. 1953. Biological stains. 6th ed. Biotechnical Publications, Geneva, N. Y. A short section on history. Extensive bibliography.

1749. **Duclaux, E.** 1898. Traité de Microbiologie. Masson et Cie, Paris. Excellent section on "Méthodes de coloration," with the important references to the work of Weigert (1877), Koch (1881), Buchner (1884), Neisser (1884), Löffler, Ehrlich (1882), Gram (1885), Baumgarten (1882), Roux (1887), and many others.

1750. **Ford, W. W.** 1939. Bacteriology. Paul B. Hoeber, Inc., New York. Historical information on staining scattered in various sections of the book.

1751. **Smith, E. F.** 1905. Bacteria in relation to plant diseases. Published by Carnegie Institution of Washington, Washington, D. C. Excellent listing of references of historical importance, pp. 215-221.

1752. **Sternberg, G. M.** 1893. A manual of bacteriology. William Wood & Co., New York. Bibliography on staining, p. 771, is useful.

Journal:

1753. **Stain technology.** 1926--date. A journal for microtechnic. Biotech. Publications, Geneva, N. Y. Sections devoted to abstracts of books and papers from other journals dealing with stains and microscopic techniques in general.

1754. **Unna, P. G.** 1888. Die Entwickelungder Bacterienfärbung. Eine historischkritische Ubersicht. Centralbl. f. Bakteriol., 3, 22-26, 61-63, 93-99, 120-125, 153-158, 189-195, 218-221, 254-259, 285-291, 312-320, 345-348. Detailed history of staining found in Unna's articles. At the end, 71 papers on this subject are cited.

79

TECHNOLOGY

See general broad listings in:

1764. **Russo, F.** 1954. Histoire des Sciences et des Techniques. Bibliographie. Herman & Cie, Éditeurs, Paris.

1765. Sarton, G. 1952. Horus. A guide to the history of science. A Chronica Botanica Publication. The Ronald Press Co., New York.

Also note the tremendous publication by:

1766. Forbes, R. J. 1955. Studies in ancient technology. Vol. I, 195 pp.; vol. II, 215 pp.; vol. III, 268 pp. E. J. Briel, Leiden. See review by White, L. 1957. Isis, 48, 77. There are several interesting areas for bacteriologists, e.g., ancient water supplies, alcoholic beverages, vinegar, food in general, preservation processes, etc.
1767. Singer, C. J. et al. (eds.). A history of technology. 5 vols. Oxford, At the Clarendon Press, London. Vol. I, 1954, 827 pp.; vol. II, 1956, 802 pp.; vol III, 1957, 804 pp.

The following selective list may be of some interest to the bacteriologist:

1768. Auerbach, F. 1927. The Zeiss works and the Carl Zeiss foundation in Jena: their scientific, technical and sociological development and importance popularly described. Transl. from 5th German ed. by Kanthack, R. W., and Foyle, G. London.
1769. Centrifuge and Ultra-Centrifuge. See references in Dawes, B. 1952. A hundred years of biology. Gerald Duckworth & Co. Ltd., London. P. 391.
1770. Cohen, I. B. 1950. Some early tools of American science: an account of the early scientific instruments and mineralogical and biological collections in Harvard University. Harvard Univ. Press, Cambridge.
1771. Crawhall, T. C., and Lentaique, B. 1935. Science Museum, refrigeration exhibition, April–August, 1934; a brief account of the historical development of mechanical refrigeration and a descriptive catalogue of the exhibits, with notes on the basic scientific principles. His Majesty's Stationery Office, London.
1772. Farrandane, J. 1951. History of chromatography. Nature, 67, 120.
1773. Flosdorf, E. W. 1949. Freeze drying. Reinhold Publishing Corp., New York. 280 pp.
1774. Flosdorf, E. W., Hull, L. W., and Mudd, S. 1945. Drying by sublimation. Jour. Immunol., 501, 21–54.

1775. **Kohn, M.** 1950. Remarks on the history of laboratory burners. Jour. Chem. Ed., 27, 514–516.

1776. **Moore, D. H.** 1950. Centrifugation. *In* Medical physics. Ed. by Glasser, O. The Year Book Publishers Inc., Chicago.

1777. **Phillips, C. J.** 1941. Glass: the miracle maker. Its history, technology and applications. Pitman Publishing Co., New York.

1778. **Schaefer, G.** 1947. Historical facts concerning the production and use of soap. Ciba Rev., 56, 2014–2023.

1779. **Svedberg, T.,** and **Pedersen, K. O.** 1940. The ultra-centrifuge. The Clarendon Press, Oxford.

1780. **Symposium.** 1951. Symposium on freezing and drying. Institute of Biology, London.

1781. **Weil, H.** 1950. History of chromatography. Nature, 166, 1000–1001.

1782. **Whipple, R. S.** 1939. Instruments in science and industry. Nature, 144, 461–465.

1783. **Zechmeister, L.** 1951. Early history of chromatography. Nature, 167, 405.

80

TOXINS

1793. **van Heyningen, W. E.** 1950. Bacterial toxins. C. C Thomas, Publishers, Springfield, Ill. 133 pp. An excellent monograph with a valuable listing of references, pp. 103–123. A brief historical approach in each chapter. A fine source for a historical study.

The following contemporary reviews are listed but have limited value:

1794. **Pillemer, L.,** and **Robbins, K. O.** 1949. Chemistry of toxins. Ann. Rev. Microbiol., 3, 265–288.

1795. **Symposium.** 1955. Mechanisms of microbial pathogenicity. 5th Symposium, Soc. Gen. Microbiology. At the Univer-

sity Press, Cambridge. 333 pp. Articles by van
Heyningen, W. E., pp. 17–39; Macfarlane, M. G., pp. 57–
77; Wright, G. P., pp. 78–102.

81

VETERINARY

The history of veterinary bacteriology is closely associated with the history of medical bacteriology. See
Bulloch's book.

In addition, see:

1805. **Sarton, G.** 1952. Horus. A guide to the history of science.
A Chronica Botanica Publication. The Ronald Press Co.,
New York. See section, "History of veterinary medi-
cine," p. 191, for general historical references. In ad-
dition add:
Bierer, B. W. 1955. A short history of veterinary
medicine in America. Michigan State Univ. Press.
113 pp.
Leyman, C. P. 1898. History of veterinary medicine.
Cambridge.
Neffgen, H. 1904. Das Veterinär—Papyrus von
Kahun. Berlin.

The following texts have some historical material:

1806. **Buchanan, R. E.** 1911. Veterinary bacteriology. W. B.
Saunders Co., Philadelphia. 516 pp. An early publication based on the lectures given at Iowa State College.
1807. **Kelser, R. A.**, and **Schoening, H. W.** 1948. Manual of veterinary bacteriology. 5th ed. Williams & Wilkins Co.,
Baltimore. This is one of the earlier classics in this
line. 1st ed., 1927.
1808. **Merchant, I. A.** 1950. Veterinary bacteriology and virology. 4th ed. Iowa State College Press, Ames, Ia. Short
section on history.

Also:

1809. **Hull, T. G.** 1930. Diseases transmitted from animals to
man. C. C Thomas, Springfield, Ill. 3d ed. 1947.
571 pp. Short section on history.

82

VIRUSES

ANIMAL AND PLANT

1819. **Bawden, F. C.** 1950. Plant viruses and virus diseases.
3d ed. A Chronica Botanica Publication. The Ronald
Press Co., New York. 335 pp. Short section on history
of virology, with emphasis on plant viruses. Excellent
listing of references.

1820. **Bulloch, W.** 1930. The history of bacteriology. *In* A
system of bacteriology. Medical Research Council,
H.M.S.O., London. Vol. I. Section, "Researches of
Pasteur on attenuation of virus and prophylactic inoculation," pp. 79–85.

1821. ———. 1938. The history of bacteriology. Oxford
Univ. Press, London. Chapter X, "Pasteur's work on
attenuation of virus," pp. 241–252.

1822. **Burnet, F. M.** 1955. Principles of animal virology. Academic Press, Inc., New York. 486 pp. Short chapter on
the historical introductions to animal virology, pp. 1–32.

1823. **Clark, P. F.** 1938. Alice in virusland. Soc. of American
bacteriologists. Univ. of Wisconsin, Madison, Wis. 23
pp. All bacteriologists should read this.

1824. **Cook, M. T.** 1947. Viruses and virus diseases of plants.
Burgess Publishing Co., Minneapolis. 244 pp. Cook is
one of the pioneers of plant pathology and has an excellent historical introduction, pp. 1–14. In addition, in
the appendix, pp. 190–195, he has a very valuable,
"Chronology of the most important discoveries and
events in the progress of our knowledge of the virus
disease of plants." A bibliography of some 1400 titles

is intended as a historical review and guide from 1576–1940.

1825. *Hallauer, C. 1950. Handbuch der Virusforschung. II Ergänzungsband. Springer-Verlag, Vienna, Austria.

1826. Holmes, F. O. 1939. Handbook of phytopathogenic viruses. Burgess Publishing Co., Minneapolis, Minn. Small handbook with bibliography.

1827. Levaditi, C., and Lepine, P. 1948. Les ultravirus des maladies humaines. 2 vols. Libraire Maloine, Paris. 1180 pp.

1828. Luria, S. E. 1953. General virology. John Wiley & Sons, Inc., New York. Short history, pp. 5–7. Excellent bibliography, pp. 375–413.

1829. Matthews, R. E. F. 1957. Plant virus serology. Cambridge Univ. Press. 128 pp. Excellent little volume of laboratory methods in plant virology.

1830. van Rooyen, C. E., and Rhodes, A. J. 1949. Virus diseases of man. Oxford Univ. Press. 1,202 pp. An excellent reference book on the medical aspects. Short historical introduction and short historical sections. The best listing of references in the English language.

1831. Smith, K. M. 1940. The virus. Cambridge Univ. Press. The history of virus study is discussed in simple language.

1832. ———. 1948. Plant viruses. Methuen & Co., Ltd., London. 78 pp. A fine short historical discussion of the economic importance of plant virology.

1833. Stanley, W. M. 1937. Crystalline tobacco-mosaic virus protein. Amer. J. Bot., 24, 59–68. Valuable bibliography.

1834. ———. 1948. Achievement and promise in virus research. Am. Scientist, 36, 59–68.

1835. System of Bacteriology. 1929–1931. In relation to medicine. Vol. 7. Virus diseases; bacteriophage. Medical Research Council, H.M.S.O., London. Excellent source for early references.

Also see **Insect**.

There are numerous reviews and symposiums of contemporary importance not listed.

BACTERIAL

1845. **Flu, P. C.** 1946. The bacteriophage. A historical and critical survey of 25 years research. Acta Leidensia, vol. 17. Leiden.

1846. **d'Herelle, F.** 1926. The bacteriophage and its behavior. Transl. by Smith, G. H. Williams & Wilkins Co., Baltimore. 629 pp. This is the classic. A historical introduction, pp. 1–34, with an extensive bibliography, pp. 579–629.

1847. ———. 1930. The bacteriophage and its clinical applications. Transl. by Smith, G. H. C. C Thomas, Publishers, Springfield, Ill. 254 pp.

1848. **Lwoff, A.** 1953. Lysogeny. Bact. Revs., 17, 269–337. An excellent historical section, pp. 273–280.

1849. **Twort, F. W.** 1949. The discovery of the bacteriophage. Science News, 14, 33.

TECHNIQUES

Chick Embryo

1859. **Beveridge, W. I. B.,** and **Burnet, F. M.** 1946. The cultivation of viruses and rickettsiae in the chick embryo. H.M.S.O., London. 92 pp. Excellent historical introduction with fine listing of references.

1860. **Symposium.** 1952. The chick embryo in biological research. Annals N. Y. Acad. Sciences, 55, 37–344. A contemporary review with some references of historical importance.

Tissue Culture

1870. **Bibliography.** 1953. The propagation of viruses in tissue culture. Microbiological Associates, Bethesda, Md.

1871. **Bibliography of the Research in Tissue Culture, 1884–1950.** 1953. Prep. by Murray, M. R., and Kopech, G. Academic Press, Inc., New York. 2 vols. 1741 pp. Supplementary author list, 1950, 11 pp.

1872. **Ross, J. D.,** and **Syverton, J. T.** 1957. Use of tissue cultures in virus research. Ann. Rev. Microbiol., 11, 497–508.

1873. White, P. R. 1954. The cultivation of animal and plant
      cells. The Ronald Press Co., New York. Chapter 2,
      "The history of cell culture," pp. 11–31. Bibliography,
      pp. 203–218.
1874. Wilmer, E. H. 1954. Tissue culture. Methuen & Co.,
      Ltd., London. A valuable list of reference books, etc.,
      on tissue culture and cognate subjects, p. 143, and an
      excellent listing of references, pp. 144–168.

83

WARFARE

1884. Bibliography. 1952. Bacteriological warfare: A list of ref-
      erences in Soviet publications, 1929 to February 1952.
      Library of Congress, Washington, D. C. Seventy-eight
      references.
1885. Bibliography. 1952. Technical library bibliography on
      biological warfare. Camp Detrick, Frederick, Md. 27 pp.
1886. *Boulier, J. 1953. Trois lettres sur le mouvement de la
      paix. Suivi de La guerre bactériologique et L'appel de
      Stockholm. Éditions de Minuit, Paris. 96 pp.
1887. Farge, Y. 1952. Rasporto sulla guerra batteriologica al
      consiglio mondiale della pace; Berlino, 1–6 luglio, 1952.
      A cura del Comitato nazionale dei partigiani della pace.
      45 pp.
1888. Newman, B. M. 1944. Japan's secret weapon. Current
      Publishing Co., New York. 223 pp. Of interest, but one
      must read it with a background for critical evaluation.
      Lacking in scientific accuracy.
1889. *ReyesSanz, E. 195?. La guerra biológica; o, Guerra de
      microbios. Prólogo del Excmo. Ir. Dr. D. Obdulio
      Fernández. Ediciones, Geos, Madrid. 415 pp.
1890. Rosebury, T. 1949. Peace or pestilence. Biological war-
      fare and how to avoid it. Whittlesey House, McGraw-Hill
      Book Co., Inc., New York. 218 pp. Mainly for the lay-
      man. The style is light but not superficial. Excellent
      listing of general references, pp. 199–210.

1891. Rosebury, T., Kabat, E. A., and Boldt, M. H. 1947. Bacterial warfare. J. Immunol., 56, 7–96. This was the
famous review withheld from publication until after the
war. Excellent coverage of the literature.

1892. Rosebury, T. *et al.* 1948. Experimental air-borne infection. Williams & Wilkins Co., Baltimore. 222 pp. Report
on some of the studies at Camp Detrick during the war
years. This book is pregnant with possibilities for
biological warfare.

Also, see:

1893. Major, R. H. 1941. Fatal partners—War and disease.
Doubleday, Doran & Co., Inc., Garden City, N. Y. 342
pp. Although this publication is not concerned directly
with bacterial warfare, it is of great value as a historical
background for this subject. References, pp. 331–335.

In addition there is an excellent listing of articles on
this subject found in:

1894. Index-Catalogue of the Library of the Surgeon General's
Office. United States Army. Government Printing Office, Washington, D. C. E.g., Fourth Series, 1955,
pp. 340–341.

84

WATER

1904. Baker, M. N. 1949. The quest for pure water. The history of water purification from the earliest records to the
twentieth century. The American Water Works Assoc.,
New York. 527 pp. This is an excellent history, with a
fine bibliography on pp. 473–510. The student will find
a treasury of authenticated information. A rare book
worthy of the bacteriologist's perusal.

1905. Blake, L. M. 1956. Water for the cities. A history of the
urban water supply problem in the United States. Syra-
cuse Univ. Press. 341 pp. An excellent background on
the American problem. Valuable notes and references,
pp. 288–331.

1906. Duclaux, E. Traité de microbiologie. Masson et Cie, Paris. Vol. 1. Several interesting historical chapters concerned with water bacteriology, with references.

1907. Fair, G. M., Geyer, J. C., and Morris, J. C. 1954. Water supply and waste-water disposal. John Wiley & Sons, Inc., New York. 974 pp. A short discussion of the history of water-borne diseases.

1908. Frankland, P., and Frankland, Mrs. P. 1894. Microorganisms in water. Longmans, Green & Co., London. The first important work in this area.

1909. Garrison, F. H. 1929. The history of drainage, irrigation, sewage-disposal and water supply. Bul. N. Y. Acad. Med., 5, 887–938. A brief sketch.

1910. Handbook. 1957. Selected biological references on water pollution control, sewage treatment, water treatment. U. S. Dept. of Health, Education, and Welfare—Public Health Service, Washington, D. C. 2d ed. 95 pp.

1911. Horrocks, W. H. 1901. An introduction to the bacteriological examination of water. J. & A. Churchill, London. One of the old texts.

1912. Morton, L. T. 1954. Garrison and Morton's medical bibliography. An annotated check-list of texts illustrating the history of medicine. 2d ed. W. J. Rawlinson, Ltd., Netherlands. Note section on State medicine: Public Health: Hygiene, pp. 140–146. Includes references to Frontinus, (35–104 A.D.), Bolton (1884), Dibdin (1897).

1913. Prescott, S. C., Winslow, C.-E. A., and McCrady, M. H. 1946. Water bacteriology. 6th ed. John Wiley & Sons, Inc., New York. 368 pp. It is intended to provide a historical and philosophical background for various methods of bacteriological examination of water. Emphasis is on the great American pioneers such as Smith, Sedgwick, Fuller, Whipple, Jordan, and many of their pupils and associates. Important historical references given. Bibliorgraphy, pp. 300–353. 1st ed., 1904.

1914. Reference Bibliography. 1949. Water, sewage and power plant engineering. Gilbert Associates, Inc., New York. 34 pp.

1915. Robins, F. W. 1946. The story of water supply. Oxford Univ. Press.

1916. Savage, W. G. 1906. The bacteriological examination of water-supplies. H. K. Lewis, London. Another old text.

1917. Sternberg, G. M. 1893. A manual of bacteriology. William
      Wood & Co., New York. Bibliography, bacteria in water,
      pp. 857-861.
1918. Whipple, G. C. 1899. The microscopy of drinking water.
      J. Wiley & Sons, Inc., New York. 300 pp. One of the
      great early classics.
1919. Wilson, G. S., and Miles, A. A. 1955. Topley and Wilson's
      principles of bacteriology and immunity. 4th ed. The
      Williams & Wilkins Co., Baltimore. Vol. II, Chapter 92,
      "The bacteriology of water, shell-fish, and sewage,"
      pp. 2284-2310, has a short summary and refers to ex-
      cellent historical sources, and lists under the references
      the standard works of the United States, Great Britain,
      France, and Argentina. Many other references of value
      listed.

Part III

BIOGRAPHICAL REFERENCES—BACTERIOLOGISTS

85

BIOGRAPHICAL COLLECTIONS—GUIDE TO

A biography is often an excellent source of information concerning a special area in bacteriology, for frequently it will contain a very complete list of his or her publications. This is true not only of book-length biographies but also in many instances found in biographical material published in a journal. The abstract journals usually list the titles of such articles and in many instances state whether it is a memorial lecture, an obituary, or biographical.

1929. **Artelt, W.** 1953. Index zur Goschichte der Medizin, Natur-wissenschaft und Technik. Urban & Schwarzenberg. München und Berlin. A very excellent source for the medical bacteriologists covering the years 1945–1948.

1930. **Biography Index.** A cumulative index to biographical material, books and magazines. January, 1946–date. 1949. Ed. by Joseph, B., and Squires, C. W. The H. W. Wilson Co., New York. This is a remarkable publication with an excellent listing of bacteriologists.

1931. **Doe, J.,** and **Marshall, M. L.** 1956. Handbook of medical library practice. American Library Assoc., Chicago. A fine listing of both general and national sources for biographies.

1932. **Jackson, L.** (ed.). 1951. Technical libraries. Their organization and management. Special Libraries Assoc., New York. A short listing of selective sources, pp. 156–157.

1933. **Morton, L. T.** 1954. Garrison and Morton's medical bibli-ography. An annotated check-list of texts illustrating the history of medicine. 2d ed. W. J. Rawlinson, Ltd., Netherlands. A remarkable comprehensive listing on medical biography, pp. 581–584.

1934. **Russo, F.** 1954. Histoire de Sciences et des Techniques. Bibliographil. Herman & Cie, Éditours, Paris. Of limited value in this area.

1935. **Sarton, G.** 1952. Horus. A guide to the history of science. A Chronica Botanica Publication. The Ronald Press Co., New York. Biographical collections, pp. 84–85.

1936. **Winchell, C. M.** (ed.). 1951. Guide to reference books. American Library Assoc., Chicago. An excellent comprehensive listing, pp. 430–451. This contains such sources as, Biography index, International who's who; Who's who in Central and East Europe; Who's who in science international; World biography; Who was who, Wer est wer; American men of science, and numerous other publications. Supplement, by Winchell, C. M., and Johnson, O. A., 1954, pp. 86–89; Supplement by Winchell, C. M., 1956, p. 55.

86

BIOGRAPHICAL INFORMATION OF BACTERIOLOGISTS

The following have been found to be the most valuable for biographical information of bacteriologists:

1946. **Bullock, W.** 1938. The history of bacteriology. Oxford Univ. Press. The section on biographical notices of some of the early workers in bacteriology, pp. 349–406, is one of the finest sources for information, with a bibliography which is outstanding. We owe so much to Bullock for bringing to our attention the almost forgotten pioneers in bacteriology.

1947. **Ford, W. W.** 1939. Bacteriology. Paul B. Hoeber, Inc., N. Y. A less comprehensive attempt but accurate and with a fine bibliography.

87

MISCELLANEOUS REFERENCES CONTAINING BIOGRAPHICAL INFORMATION

The following selected list may be of value:

1957. Allen, P. W., Holtman, D. F., and McBee, L. A. 1941. Microbes which help destroy us. C. V. Mosby Co., St. Louis. Mainly for the layman. Bibliography, pp. 531–534.

1958. Almquist, E. 1931. Grosse Biologen. Eine Geschichte der Biologie und ihrer Erforscher. J. F. Lehmanns Verlag, München. 143 pp. 23 port. Sections on Linné, Koch, Pasteur, Smith, T., and others. Reviewed by Kofoid, C. A. 1932. Isis, 18, 206–207.

1959. Baron, A. L. 1957. Man against germs. E. P. Dutton & Co., New York. 320 pp. A very interesting account.

1960. Bayne-Jones, S. 1932. Man and microbes. The Williams & Wilkins Co., Baltimore. P. 128. Not well done. Lacks a bibliography.

1961. Bigger, J. W. 1939. Man against microbe. The Macmillan Co., New York. 304 pp. A history of bacteriology that is well done, but it is merely an introduction to the subject. This is not a substitute for Bulloch's works. Reviewed by Leikind, M. C. 1949. Isis, 32, 409.

1962. Birkeland, H. 1942. Microbiology and man. Williams & Wilkins Co., Baltimore. For the layman.

1963. *Blair, I. D. 1948. Micro-organisms and human affairs. Simpson & Williams, Christchurch, N. Z.

1964. Bolton, S. K. 1946. Famous men of science. 3d ed. Revised by Sanderson, E. W. Thomas Y. Crowell Co., New York. 308 pp. A collection of biographical essays written in a popular style. Includes Linnaeus, Pasteur, Reed, etc.

1965. Cohen, B. 1950. Chronicles of the Society of American Bacteriologists, 1899–1950. Golden Jubilee Meeting, Baltimore. 83 pp. Brief notes with portraits.

1966. Conn, H. C. 1933. The history of staining. Biological Stain Commission, Geneva, N. Y. 141 pp. Includes

brief but excellent biographical notes with portraits of
the pioneers in staining, e.g., Paul Ehrlich.

1967. Dewberry, E. B. 1950. Food poisoning. Its nature, history and causation; measures for its prevention and control. Foreword by Leighton, G. R. Leonard Hill, Ltd.,
London. 315 pp. This book contains an excellent but
short account, with portraits, of the early and important
workers in this field.

1968. Drew, J. 1940. Man, microbe, and malady. Harmonds-
worth, Middlesex, England. For the layman.

1969. Hastings, E. G., and Morrey, C. B. 1918. Early instructors
in bacteriology in the United States (addenda). Jour.
Bact., 3, 307-308.

1970. Heub, T. 1947. Dentsche Gestalten. Studien zum 19.
Jahrhundert. Reiner Wunderlich Verl. Herm. Lewis,
Stuttgart E. Tübingen. Includes Semmelweis, Pet-
tenkofer, Röntgen, Behring, and others.

1971. Hitchens, A. P., and Leikind, M. C. 1939. The introduction of agar-agar into bacteriology. Jour. Bact., 37,
485-493. Frau Hesse, wife of the bacteriologist Walther
Hesse, thought of the idea of using a solid culture sub-
strate. This was communicated to Robert Koch in 1881.
"Koch recognized its value and made it his own."

1972. Howard, A. V. 1955. Chamber's dictionary of scientists.
2d ed. E. P. Dutton & Co., Inc., New York. Brief but
well done.

1973. Kelly, E. C. 1948. Encyclopedia of medical sources.
Williams & Wilkins Co., Baltimore. 476 pp. Excellent
check list for the medical bacteriologist.

1974. de Kruif, P. 1926. Microbe hunters. Harcourt, Brace &
Co., Inc., New York. 320 pp. An appetizer. Fascinat-
ing and interesting. "The heroes are the makers." In-
cludes, Leeuwenhoek, Spallanzani, Pasteur, Koch, Roux,
Behring, Metchnikoff, Theobald Smith, Bruce, Ross,
Grosse, Walter Reed, and Ehrlich.

1975. _____. 1928. Hunger fighters. Harcourt, Brace &
Co., Inc., New York. Popular. Includes Semmelweis,
Banting, Menot, Schaudin, Bordet, Wagner-Jauregg,
Spencer, Evans, McCoy.

1976. Kluyver, A. T. 1947. Three decades of progress in microbiology. Antonie van Leeuwenhoek Jour. Microbiol. and
Serol., 13, 1-20.

1977. McKee, A. P. 1957. Biblical microbiology. Bact. News, 23, 5-9.

1978. Mechnikov, I. I. *et al.* 1939. The founders of modern medicine: Pasteur, Koch, Lister. Transl. by Berger, D. Waldren Publishers, New York. 387 pp.

1979. Meisen. (ed.). 1932. Prominent Danish scientists through the ages, with facsimiles from their works. Levin & Munksgaard, Copenhagen. 195 pp. Includes, Panum, Bang, Hansen, and others. Reviewed by Sarton, G. 1935. Isis, 41, 276-278.

1980. van Niel, C. B. 1949. The "Delft School" and the rise of general microbiology. Bact. Revs., 13, 161-174. A brief but excellent presentation.

1981. Price, E. G. 1948. Fighting spotted fever in the Rockies. Naegele Printing Co., Helena, Montana. Excellent biographical material of the early workers in this field. Ricketts, etc.

1982. Rostand, J. 1945. Esquisse d'Une Histoire de la Biologie. 12th ed. Gallimard, Paris. 257 pp. Excellent. There is no comparable book to this in English. Short sketches of Redi, Leeuwenhoek, Linnaeus, Buffon, Spallanzani, Pasteur, etc.

1983. Silverman, M. 1941. Magic in a bottle. The Macmillan Co., New York. 322 pp. Of interest to bacteriologists concerning the search for germicides by Helvetius, Lister, Pasteur, Koch, Ehrlich, Hata, and von Behring. Also, section on sulphanilamides. See review by Kofoid, C. A. 1942. Isis, 33, 553-555.

1984. Stevenson, L. G. 1953. Nobel prize winners in medicine and physiology, 1901-1950. Henry Schuman, Inc., New York. 292 pp. A convenient handbook. We now need a comprehensive treatment. Includes, Behring, Koch, Metchnikoff, Ehrlich, Bordet, Nicolle, Eijkman, Landsteiner, Domagk, Fleming, and Florey.

1985. Winslow, C.-E. A. 1950. Some leaders and landmarks in the history of microbiology. Bact. Revs., 14, 99-114. An excellent service for an American background.

In addition refer to: The Index-Catalogue of the Library of the Surgeon General's Office, United States Army. Lists numerous articles, books, etc., concerning the history of bacteriology.

See also Guide for the Medical Bacteriologist; include
sections on bacteriology, immunology, epidemiology, etc.

88

AGE OF BACTERIOLOGISTS FOR BEST WORK

1994. **Adams, C. W.** 1946. The age at which scientists do their
best work. Isis, 36, 166–169. The median prime of
scientists is around 43. Bacteriologists around 38. Of
the 326 bacteriologists in the biographical notes in
Bulloch's "History of Bacteriology," 113 were born between 1850–1863. "But humans vary, as apples do,
some ripen in July, others in October."

1995. **Lehman, H. C.** 1953. Age and achievement. The Amer.
Philos. Soc., Princeton Univ. Press, Princeton, N. J.
Bibliography, pp. 333–341.

1996. _____. 1958. The chemists's most creative years.
Science, 127, 1213–1222. "The 2500 ablest of the
world's chemists attained their maximum production
rate at 30 through 34." This article includes an excellent list of references.

89

DISCOVERIES DUE TO CHANCE—BACTERIOLOGY

2005. **Beveridge, W. I. B.** 1953. The art of scientific investigation. 2d ed. William Heinemann, Ltd., London. Chap-
ter 3, Chance. Illustrates the role that chance has
played concerning a number of important bacteriological
discoveries, e.g., anaphylaxis by Dale, acid-fast method
by Ehrlich, agglutination of red blood cells by Hirst,
discovery of agglutination of bacteria by Gruber and
Durham, discovery of x-rays by Röntgen, discovery of

penicillin by Fleming, the use of the ferret in human influenza studies, the property of formalin of removing the toxicity of toxins by Ramon, the sterilization work of air by the use of glycol, Pasteur's work on fowl cholera, staining of bacteria by Gram, yolk sack method of growing Rickettsiae, etc.

2006. Farber, E. 1950. Chemical discoveries by means of analogies. Isis, 41, 20–26. See interesting brief section on dyes and drugs, Paul Ehrlich.

2007. Schaar, B. E. 1955. Some accidental scientific discoveries. Schaar & Co., Chicago. 62 pp. Sections on: the benzene ring, penicillin, radioactivity, and x-rays are of interest.

2008. Taton, R. 1955. Causalités et accidents de la découverte scientifique. Masson et Cie, Paris. 171 pp. (English transl., 1957.) This is a very stimulating and unusual publication where all historians of science will find interesting information about a number of discoveries, e.g., Names of interest: Curie, M., and Curie, P., Dubos, R., Fleming, A., Florey, H. W., Helmholtz, H., Hooke, R., Leeuwenhoek, A., Lister, J., Mendel, G., Nicolle, C., Pasteur, L., Röntgen, W. K., Ross, R., Semmelweis, I., Spallanzani, L., and Tyndall, J. Some subjects of interest such as antisepsie, antibiotiques, évolution, gènes, microbiologie, microscopie, vaccination, pyocyanase, typhus, etc.

2009. ———. 1955. Design and chance in discovery and invention. Impact of Science on Society, 6, 208–232. Stimulating discussion.

2010. Walden, P. 1951. The role of chance in chemical discoveries. Jour. Chem. Ed., 28, 304–308.

Part IV

SELECTIVE GUIDE TO BIOGRAPHIES OF
SELECTED BACTERIOLOGISTS

The following biographical references are merely selective and supplement Bulloch's work. The reader should also refer to "Biography Index" for numerous contemporary references.

90

BEHRING, E. A. von

German bacteriologist, 1854–1917. Discoverer of antitoxin and the principles of serotherapy. Nobel prize
winner.

2020. Artelt, W. 1953. Index zur Geschichte der Medizin,
Naturwissenschaft und Technik. Urban & Schwarzenberg.
München und Berlin. Excellent listings of articles from
1945–1948 written about Behring, pp. 117–118.

2021. (Behring, Emil von). 1940, 1941/42. A great many publications appeared in Germany in 1940 to celebrate the
fiftieth anniversary of the discovery of serum therapy by
Emil v. Behring in 1890. For a list of them and reviews
of the most important, see: Mitteilungen zur Geschichte
der Medizin, 39, 260–265 (1949), and 40, 245 (1941/42).

2022. *Behring zum Gedächtnes. 1942. Reden und Wissenschaftliche Vorträge. Anlässlich der Behring-Erinne-
rungsfeier. Bruno Schultz Verlag, Grunewald, Berlin.

2023. Helmuth, E. v. 1948. Emil von Behring. Sein Leberswerk
als unvergaengliches. Ungr, Hamburg.

2024. Stevenson, L. G. 1953. Nobel prize winners in medicine
and physiology, 1901–1950. Henry Schuman, Inc., New
York. Behring, pp. 3–9. Port.

2025. Unger, H. 1948. Emil von Behring. Sein Lebenswerk als
unvergängliches Erbe. Hoffmann und Campe, Hamburg.
245 pp. A fine study.

2026. Zeiss, H., and Bieling, R. 1940. Behring. Gestalt und
Werk. Schultz, Berlin. 627 pp. One of the best studies.
See review by Neander, G. 1941. Lychnos, 420–421.

*A study or a translation in the English language is definitely
needed.

91

BEIJERINCK, M. W.

Dutch microbiologist, 1851–1931. Considered by many as one of the big four in bacteriology, along with Winogradsky, Pasteur, and Koch. He was a prodigious worker with superb powers of observation. Noted for his basic important work in soil bacteriology, specifically cycles, physiology, and also plant infections.

2036. Beijerinck, M. W. 1921–1946. Verzamelde Geschriften. 6 vols. Delft, Holland. His collected writings.
2037. van Iterson, G., Jr., Den Dooren De Jong, L. E., and Kluyver, A. J. 1940. Martinus Willem Beijerinck. His life and his work. Nijhoff, The Hague. 193 pp. A well-illustrated biography.

92

BIGGS, HERMAN M.

1859–1923. A pioneer in the public health aspects of bacteriology and immunology of the 80's and 90's in America.

2047. Winslow, C.-E. A. 1929. The life of Hermann M. Biggs (1859–1923), M. D., D. Sc., L.L.D., Phycician and statesman of the public health. Lea & Febiger, Philadelphia. 432 pp. An excellent presentation of Bigg's professional work and personality.

93

BILLROTH, (CHRISTIAN ALBERT) THEODOR

1829–1894. Noted for his work in surgical pathology. Unfortunately, his interpretation of surgical infections was wrong.

2057. *Billroth, Theodor (1829-1894). 1935. Billroth und Brahms im Briefwechsel. Mit Einleitung. Anmerkungen und 4 Bildtafeln. Urban u. Schwarzenberg, Berlin. 528 pp.

2058. Brunn, W. v. 1936. Theodor Billroth. Sonderdruck aus der Münchener Medizinischen Wochenschrift, No. 22. 11 pp. Port.

94

BORDET, JULES

Belgian bacteriologist, 1870–   . Received the Nobel Prize in 1919. He did much to enrich the fields of medical bacteriology and immunology. It is unfortunate that so little has been written about this great immunologist.

2067. Fleming, A. 1950. Homage on behalf of foreign scientists. Ann. Inst. Pasteur, 79, 495-498.

2068. Renaux, E. 1950. Eightieth birthday. Ann. Inst. Pasteur, 79, 479-491. Special number celebrating eightieth birthday. Bordet, J. 1950. Ann. Inst. Pasteur, 79, 479-813.

2069. Stevenson, L. G. 1953. Nobel Prize winners in medicine and physiology, 1901-1950. Henry Schuman, Inc., New York. Brief section on Jules Bordet. We now need a comprehensive treatment. Received the Nobel prize "For his discoveries in regard to immunity."

95

BUFFON, GEORGES L. L.

French writer on natural history, 1707-1788. Along with Needham he developed the doctrine of organic molecules in reference to the origin of life.

2079. Brown, H. 1947. Buffon and the Royal Society of London. Studies and essays offered to George Sarton. Henry Schuman, Inc., New York. Pp. 137-165.

2080. *Dimier, L. 1919. Buffon. Nouvelle librairie nationale,
Paris.
2081. Falls, W. F. 1939. Buffon et les premières bêtes du
Jardin du Roi: Histoire ou légende? Isis, 30, 491-494.
2082. Matousek, A. 1950. Buffon and the philosophy of his
natural history. Arch. internationales d'hist des
sciences, 29, 312-319.
2083. *Michant, G. 1931. Buffon administrateur et homme d'af-
faires. Lettres inédites. Annales de l'Univ. de Paris,
6, 15-36.
2084. Roule, L. 1924. Buffon et la description de la nautre. E.
Flammarion, Paris. 248 pp. Reviewed by Kofoid, C. A.
1935. Isis, 23, 264-265.

96

CALMETTE, ALBERT L. C.

French bacteriologist, 1863-1933. One of Pasteur's il-
lustrious pupils. Discoverer of the antivenin serum and the
BCG vaccine.

2094. Bernard, N., and Negre, L. 1940. Albert Calmette, sa vie,
son oeuvre scientifique. Masson et Cie, Paris. This is
a very interesting biography and the only one written on
this important figure in bacteriology.

97

CHAIN, ERNST BORIS

Chemist, 1906-

2104. Stevenson, L. G. 1953. Nobel prize winners in medicine
and physiology, 1901-1950. Henry Schuman, Inc., New
York. Pp. 229-237. Chain with Fleming and Florey
shared the Nobel prize "For the discovery of penicillin
and its therapeutic effect for the cure of different infectious maladies."

98

COHN, F.

One of the founders of bacteriology, 1828–1898.

2114. Cohn, F. 1872. Bacteria, the smallest of living organisms. Transl. by Dolley, C. S. 1881. Introduction by Leikind, M. C. 1939. The Johns Hopkins Press, Baltimore. A classic. Bibliography of Ferdinand Cohn, pp. 40–44.

99

DOMAGK, GERHARD

German bacteriologist, 1895–   . Discoverer of sulphanilamide. Nobel Prize winner.

2124. Long, P. H. 1940. Award of the Nobel prize in physiology and medicine to Dr. Gerhard Domagk. Scientific Monthly, 50, 83–84.
2125. Stevenson, L. G. 1953. Nobel prize winners in medicine and physiology, 1901–1950. Henry Schuman, Inc., New York. Short account, pp. 209–214. Port. Received the Nobel prize "For his discovery of the antibacterial effects of prontosil."

100

DUCLAUX, ÉMILE P.

French bacteriologist, 1840–1904. One of Pasteur's great assistants. Published much in bacteriology. Succeeded Pasteur as Director of the Pasteur Institute.

2135. Duclaux, Madame É. 1906. La vie de Émile Duclaux. L. Barneound & Cie, Paris. A good biography, but much is needed.

101

EHRLICH, PAUL

German scientist, 1854–1915. One of the greatest of all times. Noted for numerous important discoveries in bacteriology, immunology, and chemotherapy. Received the Nobel prize "In recognition of his work on immunity."

2145. Ehrlich, P. (1854–1915). 1914. Eine Darstellung seines wissenschaftlichen Wirkens, Festschrift zum 60. Geburtstage des Forschers 14 März 1914. Gustav Fischer, Jena. Ehrlich's work from the scientific standpoint. The best source for a study of his work. An outstanding contribution of this remarkable man dedicated to him on his sixtieth birthday.

2146. _____. Collected papers. 1955. Compiled and edited by Himmelweit, F., with the assistance of Marquardt, M. 4 vols. London and New York. The majority of the papers are in German, with some in English and a few in French. An English translation accompanies German treaties of greatest importance. Vol I, 635 pp.; vol II, 1957; vols. III and IV to appear in 1958.

2147. Lazarus, A. 1922. Paul Ehrlich. Meister der Heilkunde, 2. mit einem Bildnis Ehrlichs. Rikola, Wien. 88 pp. A small volume giving a clear and comprehensive account of his life and work.

2148. *Loewe, H. 1950. Paul Ehrlich, Schöpfer der Chemotherapie. Wissenschaftliche Verlagsgesellschaft, Stuttgart, Berlin.

2149. Marquardt, M. 1924. Paul Ehrlich (1854–1915), als Mensch und Arbeiter. Deutsche Verlagsgesellschaft, Stuttgart, Berlin. 112 pp. A brief biography in German. Four ports.

2150. _____. 1951. Paul Ehrlich. Introduction by Sir Henry Dale. Henry Schuman, Inc., New York. 255 pp. A vivid account of Ehrlich's character. The author was Ehrlich's secretary from 1902 to his death in 1915. A very readable and stimulating biography. Book lacks an index. Unfortunately there is no full bibliography of Ehrlich's publications.

2151. **Muir, R.** 1915/16. Paul Ehrlich. Jour. Path. & Bact., 20, 350–360.
2152. **Stevenson, L. G.** 1953. Nobel prize winners in medicine and physiology, 1901–1950. Henry Schuman, Inc., New York. A brief section, pp. 51–56. Port.
2153. **Venzmer, G. V.** 1948. Paul Ehrlich, Leben und Wirken. Mundus-Verlag, Stuttgart, Germany. 94 pp.

102

ENDERS, JOHN F.

1897–   . Nobel Prize winner for physiology and medicine, 1954. Basic important work in tissue culture studies which led to the practical application in reference to the "Polio" vaccine.

2163. **Biography.** Cur. Biog. Yrbk. Port. 1955. Pp. 182–183.; Cur. Biog., 16, 23–25 (1955); Am. Ann., pp. 228–229 (1955).
2164. **Nobel Prize for Physiology and Medicine.** 1954. Nature, 174, 818.
2165. Newsweek, 44, 63 (1954).
2166. Time, 64, 77 (1954).
2167. Lasker award winners who later won the Nobel prize. Port. 1956. Vogue, 127, 171.

103

EIJKMAN, C.

Dutch bacteriologist, 1858–1930.

2177. **Stevenson, L. G.** 1953. Nobel prize winners in medicine and physiology, 1901–1950. Henry Schuman, Inc., New York. Pp. 134–142. Port. Received the Nobel prize "For his discovery of the antineuritic vitamin."

104

FIBIGER, J. A. G.

Danish bacteriologist, 1867–1928.

2187. **Stevenson, L. G.** 1953. Nobel prize winners in medicine and physiology, 1901–1950. Henry Schuman, Inc., New York. Pp. 120–124. Port. Received the Nobel prize "For his discovery of the Spiroptera carcinoma." His work resulted in a clear-cut confirmation of the view of Rudolf Circhow, that cancerous growths are due to chronic irritation.

105

FINLAY, CARLOS J.

1833–1915. Mosquitoes and yellow fever.

2197. *Finlay, C. E. 1940. Carlos Finlay and yellow fever. Oxford University Press, New York.
2198. **Finlay, C. J.** 1938. Medical Classics, 2, 540–619. Excellent biography and bibliography.
2199. **Givhan, E. G.** 1939. Carlos Finlay (1833–1910). Annals Med. Hist., 1, 189–193. Many articles have been written about Finlay.

106

FLEMING, ALEXANDER

Scottish bacteriologist, 1881–1955. Discoverer of penicillin.

2209. **Ludovici, L. J.** 1952. Fleming; discoverer of penicillin. Andrew Dakers, London. 223 pp. This is an interesting

story, but more will have to be written. Note review by
Welsch, M. 1953. Arch. int. Hist. Sci., 32, 351-352.

2210. **Robinson, D. B.** 1952. 100 most important people in the
world today. Pocket Bks., Inc. Pp. 280-283. Port.

2211. **Stevenson, L. G.** 1953. Nobel prize winners in medicine
and physiology, 1901-1950. Henry Schuman, Inc., New
York. Pp. 229-237. Port.

Many articles have been written about Fleming.

107

FLOREY, HOWARD W.

Australian physiologist, 1898–   . Nobel prize winner
for his work on penicillin.

2221. **Stevenson, L. G.** 1953. Nobel prize winners in medicine
and physiology, 1901-1950. Henry Schuman, Inc., New
York. Pp. 229-237. Port.

There are many other articles.

108

FRACASTORO, GIROLAMO

Italian physician, humanist, poet, astronomer, etc.,
1478-1553.

2231. **Baumgartner, L., and Fulton, J. F.** 1935. A bibliography
of the poem syphilus—Sive Morbus Gallicus by Girolamo
Fracastoro of Verona. Yale Univ. Press. 157 pp. An
outstanding piece of work. Note review by Sarton, G.
1935. Isis, 24, 437-439.

2232. **Pellegrini, F.** 1940. La dottrina fracastorianna del
"contagium vivum" Origini e primi sviluppi tratti da

autografi inediti conservati nella biblioteca capitolare
di Verona. Verona. 90 pp. Review by Coisini, A. 1950.
Rivista di storia delle scienze anno 41, 229.

2233. _____. 1948. Girolamo Fracastoro. (Collana di
Vite di Medici e Naturalisti celebri, 3). Zigiotti,
Trieste. 186 pp. General study of Fracastora: Biography, the physician, the naturalist, the philosopher, the
poet, bibliography. No index. See reviews by: Sarton,
G. 1952. Isis, 43, 137. Giugni, F. 1948. Rivista di
storia delle scienze, anno 39, 215.

109

GORGAS, WILLIAM C.

1854–1920. Yellow fever and the Panama Canal.

2242. **Gibson, J. M.** 1950. Physician to the world. Duke University Press. 315 pp. An interesting intimate account.
An extensive bibliography.

2243. **Gorgas, M. D.,** and **Hendrick, B. J.** 1924. William Crawford Gorgas: His life and work. Garden City Publishing
Co., Inc., Garden City, N. Y. An interesting account.

2244. **Gorgas, William Crawford** (1854–1920). 1924. Whole
number of Medical Life, 31, 419–460 devoted to him.
Numerous ports.

2245. **Martin, T. W.** 1947. Doctor William Crawford Gorgas of
Alabama and the Panama Canal. Newcomen Soc., Amer.
Branch, New York.

110

HANSEN, GERHARD HENRIK ARMAUER

Norwegian leprologist, 1841–1912. Discovered the
leprosy bacillus.

2255. **Kobro, I.** 1925. Gerhard Henrik Armauer Hansen (1841–
1912). Annals of Med. Hist., 7, 127–132.

There are other articles on Hansen, but much more is needed.

111

HENLE, (FRIEDRICH GUSTAV) JACOB

German pathologist (1809–1885) who in 1840 made a remarkable anticipation of the germ theory of disease.

2265. Haberling, W. 1929. From the life of Jacob Henle. Medical Life, 36, 501–507.
2266. Henle, J. On miasmata and contagia. Transl. by Rosen, G. 1938. The Johns Hopkins Press, Baltimore. 77 pp. One of the great classics.
2267. Robinson, V. 1921. The life of Jacob Henle (1809–1885). Medical Life Co., New York. A short but interesting account.

112

d'HERELLE, FELIX-HUBERT

Canadian-born bacteriologist, 1873–1949. Noted for his work on bacteriophage.

2277. Compton, A. 1949. Prof. Felix d'Herelle. Nature, 163, 984–985. d'Herelle, F. (1873–1949). 1949. Am. Med. Assn. J., 140, 907. Much more is needed.

113

KITASATO, SHIBASABURO

Japanese bacteriologist, 1852–1931. Noted for his work with Behring on tetanus antitoxin. First cultivated *Cl. tetani*. Discovered the plague bacillus.

2287. **Fox, H.** 1934. Baron Shibasaburo Kitasato. Annals Med. Hist., 6, 491–499.
2288. **Kitasato, Shibasaburo.** 1931. The passing of Kitasato. Medical Life, 519–520. Port.
2289. **Miyajima, M.** 1931. Shibasaburo Kitasato. Science, 74, 124–215.

More is needed.

114

KOCH, ROBERT

German bacteriologist, 1843–1910. One of the greatest laboratory technicians in bacteriology of all times. He received the Nobel prize "For his investigations and discoveries in regard to tuberculosis." There does not exist any full-size biography of Robert Koch in the English language.

2299. *Becher, W. 1891. Robert Koch: Eine biographische Studie. Konitzer, Berlin.
2300. **Bochalli, R.** 1954. Robert Koch Wissenschaftliche Verlagsgesellschaft, Stuttgart. 216 pp. Review by Lagrange, E. 1954. Arch. int. Hist. Sci., 33, 221–223.
2301. **Brown, L.** 1935. Robert Koch (1843–1910). An American tribute. Part I, Annals Med. Hist., 7, 99–112. Part II–III, 7, 292–304; 385–401.
2302. **Burke, R. M.** 1938. A historical chronology of tuberculosis. C. C Thomas, Publishers, Springfield, Ill. Excellent account of Koch's discovery.
2303. **Cummins, S. L.** 1949. Tuberculosis in history. From the 17th century to our own times. Baillière, Tindall & Cox, London. Fine section on the history and achievements of Robert Koch.
2304. **Drigalski, W. v.** 1948. Im Wirkungsfelde Robert Kochs. Dulk, Hamburg, 523 pp.
2305. **Ford, W. W.** 1911. The life and work of Robert Koch. Bul. Johns Hopkins Hosp., 22, 415–424.

2306. **Heymann, B.** 1932. Robert Koch. Teil 1: 1843–1882.
(Grosse Männer: Studien zur Biologie des Genies.)
Akademische Verlagsgesellschaft, Leipzig. 353 pp.
This is probably the best work on Robert Koch pub-
lished.

2307. **King, L. S.** 1952. Dr. Koch's postulates. J. Hist. Med.,
7, 350–361. Koch's postulates can be understood only
in relation to the problems current at the time.

2308. ***Kirchner, M.** 1924. Robert Koch. Vienna.

2309. **Koch, R.** 1912. Gesammelte Werke von Robert Koch. 2
vols. G. Thieme, Leipzig. Actually 2 vols in 3 of the
remarkable work of one of the greatest bacteriologists
of his day.

2310. ———. 1932. From Robert Koch's investigations of
pathogenic organisms. Medical Life, 39, 175–187.

2311. ———. 1938. Biography and bibliography of biographies and writings, etc. (The etiology of anthrax, 1877.
The etiology of tuberculosis, 1882. By Koch, R., with
English translation). This is an extremely valuable
piece of work.

2312. **Koch-Bochalli, R.** 1954. Robert Koch. Der Schoepfer
der modernen Bakteriologie. Stuttgart.

2313. **Lagrange, É.** 1938. Robert Koch. Sa vie et son oeuvre.
Legrand, Paris.

2314. **Landis, H. R. M.** 1932. The reception of Koch's discovery
in the United States. Annals Med. Hist., 4, 531–537.

2315. ***Löbel, J.** 1935. Robert Koch: Geschichte eines
Glücklichen. Zurich.

2316. **Möllers, B. J.** 1950. Robert Koch; Persönlichkeit und
Lebenswerk, 1843–1910. Schmorl und von Seefeld,
Nachf, Hannover. 756 pp. Review by Fischer, G.
1952. Lychnos, 447–448.

2317. **Podach, E. F.** 1947. Robert Koch; Volk und Wissen.
Leipzig, Berlin. 84 pp.

2318. **Robinson, V.** 1924. Robert Koch (1843–1910). Medical
Life, 31, 334–374. "This essay originally appeared in
Medical Life (September, 1924) and in Chapter XVII of
Pathfinders in Medicine (1929). Republished, with a
new illustration, in commemoration of the fiftieth
anniversary of Robert Koch's discovery of the tubercle
bacillus." Excellent biography. Numerous portraits.

2319. **Smith, Theobald.** 1932. Koch's views on the stability of species among bacteria. Annals Med. Hist., 4, 524–530.

2320. **Stevenson, L. G.** 1953. Nobel prize winners in medicine and physiology, 1901–1950. Henry Schuman, Inc., New York. Pp. 25–31. Port.

2321. **Stützer, H. A.** 1947. Robert Koch. Murnau, München: Lux-Jugend-Lesebogen. 29s.

2322. **Wezel, K.** 1912. Robert Koch. Eine biographische Studie. Aug. Hirschwald, Berlin. 148 pp. Port. An excellent biography.

115

LANDSTEINER, KARL

1868–1943. Born in Vienna but studied and did most of his work in the United States. Nobel prize winner.

2332. **Boyd, W. C.** 1944. Landsteiner, K. 1868–1943. Biography bibliography. Jour. Immunol., 48, 1–16.

2333. **Stevenson, L. G.** 1953. Nobel prize winners in medicine and physiology 1901–1950. Henry Schuman, Inc., New York. Pp. 143–148. Received the Nobel prize "For his discovery of the human blood groups."

Much more is needed.

116

van LEEUWENHOEK, ANTONY

Great Dutch microscopist, 1632–1723. Father of bacteriology.

2343. **Dobell, C.** 1932. Antony van Leeuwenhoek and his "Little Animals." Staples Press, Ltd., London.

435 pp. All students of bacteriology will always be
deeply indebted to the author for this painstaking
and laborious study so well done. This is a great
book.

2344. **Leeuwenhoek, Antoni van.** The collected letters of
Antoni van Leeuwenhoek. Ed., ill., and annotated
by a committee of Dutch scientists. Vol. 1, 1938; vol.
2, 1941; vol. 3, 1948; vol. 4, 1952. Swets & Zeitlinger,
Ltd., Amsterdam. In Dutch and English. A tremendous,
remarkable, and splendid work.

2345. **Schierbeck, A.** 1951. Antoni van Leeuwenhoek; Zijn
leven en zijn Werken. Vol. 2, De Tijdstroom, Lochem.
Vol. 1, 1950. 526 p. Very elaborate biography of
Leeuwenhoek written by a leading historian of science
in Holland. The two volumes contain 78 illustrations
and are well indexed.

117

LISTER, JOSEPH

Famous English surgeon and scientist, 1827–1912.

2355. **Andrews, M. L.** 1953. Lord Lister, 1827–1912. A
Wheaton & Co., Ltd., London.

2356. **Ashhurst, A. P. C.** 1927. The centenary of Lister (1827–
1927), A tale of sepsis and antisepsis. Annals Med.
Hist., 9, 206–221.

2357. **Cameron, H. C.** 1948. Joseph Lister, the friend of man.
Wm. Heinemann, Ltd., London. 180 pp. See Review
by Liljestrand, G. 1952. Lychnos, 446–447.

2358. **Cheyne, W. W.** 1925. Lister and his achievement.
Longmans, Green & Co., London. 136 pp. Short, but
well done.

2359. **Dukes, C.** 1925. Lord Lister, 1827–1912. Leonard
Parsons, London. 186 pp.

2360. **Frowde, H.** 1909. The collected papers of Joseph Baron Lister. Oxford Univ. Press. 2 vols. A very valuable source.

2361. **Godlee, R. J.** 1918. Lord Lister. Macmillan & Co., Ltd., London. 2d ed. (1st ed., 1917; 3d ed., 1924.) Clarendon Press, Oxford. 686 pp. 3d ed., 1925, Vogel, Leipzig. 351 pp.

2362. **Guthrie, D.** 1949. Lord Lister: his life and doctrine. E. & S. Livingtone, Ltd., Edinburgh. 128 pp. A short chronological report. Excellent illustrations.

2363. **Leeson, J. R.** 1927. Lister as I know him. Ballière, Tindall & Cox, London. 212 pp.

2364. **Lister, J. B.** 1909. Collected papers. Clarendon Press, Oxford.

2365. **(Lister).** 1927. Lister centenary exhibition handbook. Wellcome Historical Medical Museum, London. 216 pp.

2366. **Lister, J. B.** 1937. Medical Classics, 2, 4-101. Biography, bibliography: "Antiseptic principles in surgery. Effects of antiseptic treatment on salubrity of a surgical hospital."

2367. **Saleeby, C. W.** 1911. Modern surgery and its makers: a tribute to Listerism. Herbert & Daniel, London.

2368. **Steuerwald, W.** 1947. Joseph Lister. Ignaz P. Semmelweis. Grieshaber & Säuberlich, Stuttgart.

2369. **Thompson, C. J. S.** 1934. Lord Lister, the discoverer of antiseptic surgery. Bale, Sons & Danielsson, London. 99 pp. 2 port. A brief biography.

2370. **Truax, R.** 1944. Joseph Lister, father of modern surgery. Bobbs-Merrill, Indianapolis. 287 pp. See review by Tomkin, O. 1945. Bull. Hist., Med., 17, 109.

2371. _____. 1947. Joseph Lister, father of modern surgery. With a foreword by Lord Horder. George G. Harrap & Co., Ltd., London. 270 pp.

2372. **Turner, A. L.** (ed.). 1927. Joseph Baron Lister. Oliver & Boyd, Edinburgh and London.

2373. **Walker, K.** 1956. Joseph Lister. Hutchinson, London. 195 pp.

2374. **Wrench, G. T.** 1913. Lord Lister, his life and work. Unwin, London.

118

METCHNIKOFF, ÉLIE (Russian ILVA ILYICH)

Russian bacteriologist, 1845–1916. He did a great deal
to develop the doctrines of immunology. Nobel prize
winner.

2384. Besredka, A. 1921. Histoire d'un idée. L'oeuvre de
      Metchnikoff. Masson et Cie, Paris. 135 pp. Port. A
      brief but well-done account. See review by Guinet, L.
      1922. Isis, 4, 519–521.
2385. Elftman, A. G. 1948. Metchnikoff as a zoologist. Victor
      Robinson memorial volume, New York. Pp. 49–60.
2386. Metchnikoff, E. 1908. The prolongation of life. G. P.
      Putnam's Sons, Inc., New York. This is an interesting
      book which indicates Metchnikoff's wide interests and
      ideas.
2387. Metchnikoff, I. I. (1845–1916). 1923. Metchnikoff number
      of Medical Life, 30, 223–274. Numerous papers.
2388. Mechnikov, I. I. (1845–1916). Russian bacteriologist. 1947.
      Centenary of the birth of Ilya Ilyich Metchnikov. Isis, 38,
      101.
2389. Metchnikoff, Olga. 1920. Vie d'Élie Metchnikoff (1845–
      1916). Hachette, Paris. 272 pp. See excellent review
      by Guinet, L. 1922. Isis, 4, 519–521.
2390. ———. 1921. Life of Eli Metchnikoff, 1845–1916.
      Constable & Co., Ltd., London. Translation of above.
2391. Pavlovskii, E. N. 1952. I. I. Metchnikoff and the War-
      Medical Academy. (In Russian). Trudy Akad. Nauk
      SSSR., Inst. ist. estestvoznaniia, Mosk., 4, 325–331.
2392. Petrie, G. F. 1942. The scientific work of Élie
      Metchnikoff. Nature, 149, 547–548.
2393. Stevenson, L. G. 1953. Nobel prize winners in medicine
      and physiology, 1901–1950. Henry Schuman, Inc., New
      York. Pp. 46–51. Port. "In recognition of his work on
      immunity."
2394. Woglon, W. H. 1949. Discoverers for medicine. Yale
      Univ. Press. Pp. 145–159. Port.

2395. **Zeiss, M.** 1932. Elias Metschnikowa, Leben und Werk. Ubersetzt und bearbeitet nach der von Frau Olga Metschnikowa, geschriebenen Biographie, dem Quellenmaterial des Moskauer Metschnikow-Museums und ligenen Nachforschungen. Fischer, Jena. 169 pp. See review by C. A. K. 1933. Isis, 35, 273-274.

119

MULLER, PAUL

Chemist, 1899-

2405. **Stevenson, L. G.** 1953. Nobel prize winners in medicine and physiology, 1901-1950. Henry Schuman, Inc., New York. Pp. 225-259. Received the Nobel prize "For his discovery of the high efficacy of DDT as a contact poison against several arthropods."

120

NEISSER, ALBERT

German bacteriologist, 1855-1916. Discovered the gonococcus.

2415. **(Gonorrhea).** 1932. Gonorrhea number. I. Readings in the history of gonorrhea. Medical Life, 39, 527-588. Albert Neisser (1884, 1885, and 1890). H. C. J. Gram (1884), Ernst Bumm (1887), and others.
2416. **Goodman, H.** 1948. Albert Neisser. Victor Robinson Memorial Volume, New York. Pp. 113-115.

121

NICOLLE, CHARLES (JULES-HENRI)

French bacteriologist, 1866–1936. Proved that typhus fever is transmitted by lice.

2426. Stevenson, L. G. 1953. Nobel prize winners in medicine and physiology, 1901–1950. Henry Schuman, Inc., New York. Pp. 130–133. Port. Received the Nobel prize "For his work on typhus." More information about Nicolle is needed.

122

NOGUCHI, HIDEYO

Japanese bacteriologist, 1876–1928. Made many contributions.

2436- Eckstein, G. 1931. Noguchi. Harper & Bros., New York. 419 pp. A unique style of scientific biography. At first it seems depressing. Nevertheless it covers well the man and his work.
2437. Flexner, S. 1929. Hideyo Noguchi (1876–1928). Annual Rept. Smithsonian Institution, 595–608.
2438. Noguchi, H. 1876–1928. Collected reprints. Rockefeller Institute for Medical Research, New York.

123

PANUM, PETER LUDWIG

Danish epidemiologist, 1820–1885. Famous for his studies of measles epidemic in Faroe Isles. A classic in its field.

2448. Gafafer, W. M. 1934. Bibliographical biography of Peter Ludwig Panum (1820–1885), epidemiologist and physiologist. Bull. Inst. Hist. Med., 2, 259–280. Port.

2449. _____. 1935. Peter Ludwig Panum's observations
on the contagium of measles. Isis, 24, 90–101.
2450. Panum, P. L. 1939. Medical Classics, 3, 802–887. Biography, bibliography. Measles on the Faroe Islands,
1846.

124

PARK, WILLIAM HALLOCK

American bacteriologist and public health worker, 1863–
1939.

2460. Oliver, W. W. 1941. The man who lived for tomorrow. A
biography of William Hallock Park, M. D. E. P. Dutton &
Co., Inc., New York. 507 pp. Port. A very valuable
bibliography. See review by Leikind, M. C. 1942. Isis,
34, 39–40.

125

PASTEUR, LOUIS

Great French chemist and bacteriologist, 1822–1895.

2470. Arcieri, G. P. 1938. Agostine Bassi and Pasteur. Vigo
Press, New York.
2471. Benz, F. E. 1938. Pasteur: Knight of the laboratory.
Dodd, Mead & Co., Inc., New York. 232 pp.
2472. Blaringhem, L. 1923. Pasteur et le transformisme. Pré-
face de Costantin, J. Masson et Cie, Paris. 261 pp.
See review by Guinet, L. 1924. Isis, 6, 424–425.
2473. Bordet, J. 1902. La vie et l'oeuvre de Pasteur.
Bruxelles.
2474. Caballero, R. 1945. Pasteur. Estudio integral de sus
obras; el hombre, el filósofo, el creyente. Rosario,
Argentina. 151 pp.

2475. Compton, P. 1932. The genius of Louis Pasteur. The Macmillan Co., New York. 361 pp. Hummanitarian aspects and services to agriculture, industry, medicine, and surgery presented. Not very well documented.

2476. Conant, J. B. 1953. Pasteur's and Tyndall's study of spontaneous generation. Harvard case histories in experimental science. Also, Pasteur's study of fermentation.

2477. Delaunay, A. 1951. Pasteur et la microbiologie. (Que sais-je?, No. 467). Presses universitaires de France, Paris. See review by Tétry, A. 1952. Revue d'histoire des sciences, 5, 100.

2478. Descour, L. 1921. Pasteur, l'homme et l'oeuvre, racontés à nos enfants. Delagrave, Paris. 256 pp. English trans. by Wedd, A. F. and Wedd, B. H. 1922. London.

2479. Drivenes, O. 1947. Louis Pasteur. Med. bilete of arbeidsoppgaver. J. W. Cappelen, Oslo.

2480. Drouin, H. 1938. La vie de Pasteur. Gallimard, Paris.

2481. Dubos, R. J. 1950. Louis Pasteur—Free lance of science. Little, Brown & Co., Boston. 418 pp. One of the best books written. A remarkable source of material. A brilliant analysis of Pasteur's discoveries. As a biography, however, it is not intended to replace Réné Valléry-Radot's classic.

2482. Duclaux, E. 1896. Pasteur, Histoire d'un esprit. Charaire et Cie, Sceaux. Transl. by Smith, E. F., and Hedges, F. 1920. W. B. Saunders Co., Philadelphia. 363 pp. This is written by one of Pasteur's great students and is certainly one of the great classics about Pasteur.

2483. Fleming, G. 1886. Pasteur and his work, from an agricultural and veterinary point of view. London.

2484. Fraitot, V. 1905. Pasteur (L'oeuvre, l'homme, le savent). Paris.

2485. Frankland, P. F., and Frankland, Mrs. P. 1898. Pasteur. The Macmillan Co., New York.

2486. George, A. 1949. Pasteur. Cette brochure précise la position religieuse de Pasteur. Albin Michel, Paris. 80 pp.

2487. Hallock, G. T., and Turner, C. E. 1928. Louis Pasteur. D. C. Heath & Co., Boston. 238 pp.

2488. Herter, C. A. 1904. Influence of Pasteur on medical science. Dodd, Mead & Co., Inc., New York.

2489. Holmes, S. J. 1925. Louis Pasteur. Harcourt, Brace & Co., Inc., New York. 246 pp.

2490. Hume, E. D. 1932. Bechamp or Pasteur? A lost chapter in the history of biology. Daniel, London. 301 pp. This book should never have been written. A subsidized book of propaganda. It is fantastic! See review in Isis, 21, 404–405 (1934)!

2491. Keim, A., and Lumet, L. 1913. Pasteur, les grands hommes. Pierre Laffite & Cie, Paris. 125 pp. (1914. Frederick A. Stokes, Co., New York.)

2492. Kopaczewski, W. 1947. Pasteur et la bactériologie. Gauthier-Villars, Paris. 96 pp.

2493. Lebert, E. M. 1947. Pasteur, sa vie, son oeuvre, son influence. The Dryden Press, Inc., New York. 212 pp.

2494. Lumet, L. 1922. Pasteur, sa vie, son oeuvre. Hachette, Paris. 256 pp.

2495. Malkus, A. S. 1952. The story of Louis Pasteur; illustrated by Spier, J. Grosset & Dunlap, Inc., New York. 178 pp. A fine story for children.

2496. Mayet, C. 1941. Pasteur, ce grand homme. Desclée de Brouwer, Paris.

2497. Monder, H. 1945. Pasteur. Ed. Correa, Paris. 189 pp. See review by Ackerknecht, E. W. 1947. Bull. Hist. Med., 21, 128.

2498. Nicolle, H. 1953. Un maître de l'enquête scientifique, Louis Pasteur. La Colombe, Paris.

2499. Oulmont, C. 1945. Pensée de Pasteur. L'Inst. Pasteur de Liaboa, Lissabon. 103 pp.

2500. Paget, S. 1914. Pasteur and after Pasteur. Adam & Charles Black, London. 152 pp.

2501. (Louis) Pasteur: His life and labours. 1883. By his son-in-law. Paris. Trans. by Lady Claud Hamilton, 1885. London. (1923, D. Appleton-Century, New York).

2502. Richet, P. 1923. L'oeuvre de Pasteur. Alcan, Paris. 120 pp. See short note by L. G. 1925. Isis, 7, 238–239.

2503. Simonnet, H. 1947. L'oeuvre de Louis Pasteur. Masson et Cie, Paris. 107 pp. A concise review of Pasteur's work devoid of biographical details.

2504. Valléry-Radot, P. (ed.). 1922-1939. Oeuvres de Pasteur. Masson et Cie, Paris, Vols. 1-7. Vol. I. Dissymétric moléculaire. Vol. II. Fermentations et générations dites spontanées. Vol. III. Études sur le vinaigre et sur le vin. Vol. IV. Études sur la maladie des vers à soie. Vol. V Études sur la bière. Vol. VI. Maladies virulentes, virus-vaccins et phophylaxie de la rage. Vol. VII. Mélanges scientifiques et littéraires. This is a monumental work containing all of Pasteur's writings in books and periodicals. Forty-page bibliography and 154-page index of subjects.

2505. _____. 1947. Pasteur. Images de sa vie suivies de quelques épisodes dramatiques de sa carrière scientifique. Flammarion, Paris. 104 pp. See short note by Sarton, G. 1948. Isis, 39, 99.

2506. _____. 1950. Pasteur; abrégé [par Pasteur Valléry-Radot] de la vie de Pasteur de René Valléry-Radot. Flammarion, Paris. 250 pp.

2507. _____. 1951. Pasteur, correspondance, réunie et annotée. 4 vols. Flammarion, Paris. Ports. See Review by Caullery, M., and Pelseneer, J. 1951. Arch. internationales d'histoire des sciences, 30, 1061-1065.

2508. _____. 1954. Pasteur inconnu. Flammarion, Paris. 248 pp. An excellent account.

2509. _____. 1956. Images de la vie et de l'oeuvre de Pasteur; (documents photographiques, la plupart inéditis provenant de la collection Pasteur Valléry-Radot.) Flammarion, Paris. 161 pp.

2510. _____. 1958. Louis Pasteur, A great life in brief. Alfred A. Knopf, Inc., New York. 212 pp. One of the finest brief accounts written.

2511. Valléry-Radot, R. 1911. The life of Pasteur. (1st ed., 1900). Trans. by Mrs. R. L. Devonshire. 2 vols. R. R. S. Constable & Co., Ltd., London, and Garden City Publishing Co., Garden City, New York. 484 pp. This is considered the greatest classic as a biography of Pasteur ever written. This, along with Dubos and Duclaux, are about the best of the numerous publications.

2512. _____. 1914. Madame Pasteur. Émile Paul, Paris. (1941. Flammarion, Paris.) 163 pp. A brief but well-done account of this remarkable woman.

2513. _____. 1948. Louis Pasteur (La vie de Pasteur, Sein Leben und Werk). Übers v. Max Hedinger u. Hans Schneider). Schwarzwald Verl, Freudenstadt. Neven, Paris. 727 pp.

2514. Wood, L. N. 1948. Louis Pasteur. Julian Messner, Inc., New York. 226 pp. It is a good biography but, like many others, it adds very little if anything to our knowledge.

2515. Zweig-Winternitz, F. M. 1947. Louis Pasteur. Bild d. Lebens u. d. Werdes. Scherz, Bern. 280 pp.

126

PETTENKOFER, MAX von

1818-1901.

2525. Hume, E. E. 1925. Max von Pettenkofer's theory of the etiology of cholera, typhoid fever and other intestinal diseases. A review of his arguments and evidence. Annals of Medical History, 7, 319-353.

2526. _____. 1927. Max von Pettenkofer, his theory on the etiology of cholera, typhoid fever and other intestinal diseases: a review of his arguments and evidence. Paul B. Hoeber, Inc., New York. 142 pp. Bibliography, pp. 109-142 (285 titles). A valuable little book. See reviews by McCrae, T. 1929. Annals Med. Hist., 1, 122, and 1928 Quart. Rev. Biol., 3, 439-440.

2527. Kisskalt, K. 1948. Max von Pettenkofer. (Grosse Naturforscher, 4). Wissenschaftliche Verlagsgesellschaft, Stuttgart. 135 pp.

2528. Neustätter, O. 1925. Max Pettenkofer (1818-1901). Julius Springer, Wien.

2529. Pettenkofer, M. von (See Winslow, C.-E. A.) 1944. The conquest of epidemic disease. Princeton Univ. Press. References, pp. 393-394.

2530. _____. 1941. The value of health for a city. English transl. by Sigerist, H. E. Johns Hopkins Press, Baltimore.

2531. Sigerist, H. E. 1935. The correspondence of Max von
Pettenkofer (1818–1901). Bul. Inst. Hist. Med., 3,
607–609.

127

RAMON, G.

2541. Ramon, G. 1950. Le Principe des anatoxines et ses
applications Travaux d'Immunologie. Masson et Cie,
Paris. 231 pp. Many personal remarks in this monograph. Why and how he investigated toxins. The last
38 pages list Ramon's 622 scientific papers.

128

REDI, FRANCESCO

Italian physician, naturalist, poet, 1626–1697. Re-
membered best for his experiments discrediting the theory
of spontaneous generation.

2551. Cole, R. 1926. Francesco Redi (1626–1697), physician,
naturalist, poet. Annals Med. Hist., 8, 347–359.
2552. Redi, F. 1762. Opere. 7 vols. Remondini, Venezia.

129

REED, WALTER

1851–1902. Physician famous for his studies on yellow
fever.

2562. Kelly, H. A. 1906. Walter Reed and yellow fever.
McClure, Phillips & Co., New York.
2563. Reed, W. (1851–1902). 1925. Lectures on bacteriology
and pathology, delivered at the medical department of
George Washington University, 1897–1898. Washington,
D. C.

2564. Truby, A. E. 1943. Memoir of Walter Reed; the yellow fever episode. Paul B. Hoeber, Inc., New York.

130

RICHET, CHARLES

1850–1935.

2574. Stevenson, L. G. 1953. Nobel prize winners in medicine and physiology 1901–1950. Henry Schuman, Inc., New York. Pp. 78–83. Received the Nobel prize "In recognition of his work on anaphylaxis."

131

ROUX, ÉMILE (PIERRE-PAUL)

French bacteriologist, 1853–1933. Contributed much to bacteriology in numerous important areas of medical bacteriology.

2584. Cressoc, M. 1951. Le docteur Roux, mon oncle. Ed. L'Arche, Paris. 241 pp. The only account available. See review by Lagrange, E. 1952. Arch. int. Hist. Sci., 31, 439.

132

RUSSELL, HARRY LUMAN

American bacteriologist, 1866–1954. Pioneer in the field of dairy bacteriology.

2594. Russell, H. L. 1921. Ed. by Hastings, E. G. Brief review of Russell's scientific life. Papers on bacteriology and allied subjects by former students of Harry Luman Russell. Univ. of Wisconsin, Studies in Science, No. 2., Madison, Wis.

133

SEDGWICK, WILLIAM THOMPSON

American bacteriologist and public health worker, 1855–1921.

2604. Jordan, E. O., Whipple, G. C., and Winslow, C.-E. A. 1924. A pioneer of public health, William Thompson Sedgwick. Yale Univ. Press. 193 pp. An interesting account written by his former students and associates.

134

SEMMELWEIS, IGNATZ PHILIPP

Austrian physician. Famous for his classic work on childbed fever.

2614. Céline, L-F. 1937. Mea Culpa and the life and work of Semmelweis. Transl. from the French by Parker, R. A. Little, Brown, & Co., Boston. 175 pp. The story is most effectively told. A must! See review by Ashley Montagu, M. F. 1938. Isis, 28, 484–487.
2615. Dawson, P. M. 1924. Semmelweis, an interpretation. Annals Med. Hist., 6, 258–279.
2616. Edgar, I. I. 1939. Ignatz Philipp Semmelweis. Outline for a biography. Annals Med. Hist., 1, 74–96.

2617. **Kertész, R.** 1943. Semmelweis. Der Kämpfer für das
Leben der Mütter. Aus dem Ungarischen übertragen van
Mirza von Schüching. Rascher, Zürich. 209 pp. See
review by Bovin, E. 1944/45. Lychnos, 462–465. In
Swedish.

2618. **Murphy, F. P.** 1946. Ignaz Philipp Semmelweis (1818–
1865). An annotated bibliography. Bull. Hist. Med.,
20, 653–707.

2619. **Podach, E. F.** 1947. Ignaz Philipp Semmelweis. Volk u.
Wissen, Berlin & Leipzig. 103 pp. Volk u. Wissen.
Kurzbiogr. Leben und Schaffen. (Bib., 1948).

2620. **Semmelweis, I. P.** 1941. Medical Classics, 5, 338–775.
Biography, bibliography. First translation into English
of the entire book on childbed fever.

2621. **Sinclair, W. J.** 1909. Semmelweis: his life and doctrine.
Manchester Univ. Press, England

2622. **Slaughter, F. G.** 1950. Immortal Magyar. Semmelweis,
conqueror of childbed fever. Henry Schuman, Inc., New
York.

2623. ***Uller, T.** 1946. Semmelweis. Der Roman seines
heroischen Wirkens. Silva-Verl, Iserlohn. 395 pp.

2624. **Wiese, E. R.** 1930. Semmelweis. Annals Med. Hist., 11,
80–88.

135

SMITH, ERWIN FRINK

American plant pathologist, 1854–1927.

2634. **Rodgers, A. D.** 1952. Erwin Frink Smith. A story of
North American plant pathology. American Philosophical Society, vol 31. Independence Square, Philadelphia.
J. H. Furst Co., Baltimore. 675 pp. An outstanding
biography of a great plant bacteriologist and pathologist. It is also a history of plant pathology from its
earlier beginnings in the U. S. in the 1880's to his
death in 1927. It follows both the science and the
scientist in its growth.

2635. **True, R. H.** 1927. Erwin F. Smith, 1854–1927. Biography and list of works. Phytopathology, 17, 675–688.

136

SMITH, THEOBALD

American bacteriologist, 1859–1934. Noted for many studies, but possibly the most important was his work on Texas fever.

2645. **Smith, T.** 1937. Medical Classics, 1, 341–669. Biography, bibliography; two papers: Investigations into the nature, causation, and prevention of southern cattle fever (1891–92). A comparative study of bovine tubercle bacilli and of human bacilli from sputum (1898).

Much more is needed.

137

SPALL ANZANI, LAZZARO

Italian naturalist and great experimenter, 1729–1799. Noted for many things. In this field famous for his experiments destroying the doctrine of spontaneous generation.

2655. **Burget, G. E.** 1924. Lazzaro Spallanzani. Annals Med. Hist., 6, 177–184.
2656. **Capparoni, P.** 1941. Lazzaro Spallanzani. (I Grandi Italiani, Collana di biografie, 13). Unione Tipografico-Editrice Torinese, Torino. 283 pp. See reviews by Zaunick. 1940. Gesch. Med., 39, 259. And Castaldi, L. 1941. Rivista di Storia dell Scienze, anno 32, 114.

2657. _____. 1948. Spallanzani. U. T. E. T., Torino.
        311 pp. See short note by Sarton, G. 1949. Isis, 40,
        367–368.
2658. **Franchini, G.** 1930. Lazzaro Spallanzani (1729–1799).
        Annals Med. Hist., 11, 56–62.
2659. **Massaglia, A.** 1925. Lazzaro Spallanzani (1729–1799).
        Medical Life, 32, 149–169.
2660. **Montalenti, G.** 1928. Lazzaro Spallanzani. I curiosi
        della natura, II. Agnelli, Milan. 126 pp. Port. Biogra-
        phy and important work of Spallanzani reported.
2661. **Spallanzani, L.** (Scandiano 1729–Pavia 1799). 1920.
        Observations et expériences faites sur les animalcules
        des infusions. 2 vols. Gauthier-Villars, Paris. Vol. 1,
        106 pp.; vol. 2, 122 pp. One of the great classics.
2662. **Rostand, J.** 1951. Les origines de la biologie expéri-
        mentale et l'Abbé Spallanzani. Fasquelle Éditeurs,
        Paris. 284 pp. See reviews by Hofsten, N. von. 1953.
        Lychnos, 421–422. Titry, A. 1953. Rev. Hist. Sci., 6,
        80–81. Sarton, G. Isis, 43, 146–147.

138

STERNBERG, GEORGE MILLER

American bacteriologist, 1838–1915. Noted for numerous
studies and for his famous manual of bacteriology.

2672. **Gibson, J. M.** 1958. Soldier in white. The life of Gen-
        eral George Miller Sternberg. Duke University Press,
        Durham, N. C. 271 pp. A very valuable contribution.
2673. **Hume, E. E.** 1938. Sternberg's centenary, 1838–1938.
        Annals Med. Hist., 16, 414–416.
2674. **Schneck, J. M.** 1944. A bibliographical note on Sternberg.
        Bul. Hist. Med., 16, 414–416.
2675. **Sternberg, M. L.** 1920. George Miller Sternberg. Amer.
        Med. Assoc., Chicago. 331 pp. An excellent presenta-
        tion.

139

TWORT, FREDERICK WILLIAM

English bacteriologist, 1877–1950. He was the original discoverer of the bacteriophagic phenomena.

2685. **Fildes, P.** 1950. Frederick William Twort, 1877–1950. *In* Royal Society of London. Obituary notices of fellows of the Royal Society. Port., autograph. (No. 20). Cambridge. 1951. Pp. 505–517. Bibliography

More needed.

140

TYNDALL, JOHN

English physicist, 1820–1893. Noted for his work on fractional sterilization, essays "On the floating-matter of the air," and spontaneous generation.

2695. **Conant, J. B.** 1953. Pasteur's and Tyndall's study of spontaneous generation. Harvard case histories in experimental science. Harvard Univ. Press, Cambridge, Mass. 61 pp. Excellent study for the student.
2696. **Eve, A. S., and Creasey, C. H.** 1945. Life and work of John Tyndall. Macmillan & Co., Ltd., London. 404 pp. See review by Rayleigh, L. 1945. Nature, 156, 189–190.
2697. **Tyndall, J.** 1881. Essays on the floating matter of the air. Longmans, Green & Co., London. One of the classics.
2698. _____. 1904. Fragments of science. J. A. Hill & Co., Éd. de luxe, New York. Fermentation, spontaneous generation.
2699. **Walton, E. C.** 1949. Tyndall, J. 1820–1893. Reproductions of prints, drawings and paintings of interest in the history of physics. Am. J. Physics, 17, 86–88.
2700. **Wedd, L. A.** 1942. John Tyndall and his contribution to the theory of spontaneous generation. Annals Med. Hist., 4, 55–62.

2701. Young, H. 1935. A record of the scientific work of John
Tyndall, D.C.L.L.L.D., F.R.S. (1850–1888). Chiswick
Press, London. 38 pp. See short note by M.C.L. 1939.
Isis, 30, 156.

141

WAGNER-JAUREGG, JULIUS

1857–1940.

2711. Stevenson, L. G. 1953. Nobel prize winners in medicine
and physiology, 1901–1950. Henry Schuman, Inc., New
York. Brief section, pp. 125–129. He received the Nobel
prize "For his discovery of the therapeutic value of
malaria inoculation in the treatment of dementia
paralytica."

142

WAKSMAN, SELMAN A.

Russian-American bacteriologist, 1888–   . Noted soil
microbiologist. Discoverer of streptomycin. Nobel prize
winner.

2721. Waksman, S. A. 1954. My life with the microbes. Simon &
Schuster, Inc., New York. 364 pp. "Discovery is a sub-
tle blend of unexciting detail work, insight and good
luck." This is an interesting account of Waksman's
life but gives little insight into the scientific creative
process.

2722. Waksman, S. A. 1953. (1888–   ). Robinson, D. B. 100
most important people. 1953. Pocket Bks., Inc., New
York. Pp. 291–294. Port.

143

WEIGERT, CARL

German pathologist and histologist, 1845–1904. Noted
for his contributions of staining methods in bacteriology
and histology.

2732. Morrison, H. 1924. Carl Weigert. Annals Med. Hist., 6,
163–177.

144

WELCH, WILLIAM HENRY

American bacteriologist, 1850–1934. Famous teacher at
Johns Hopkins Medical School.

2742. The Account of the Origin and Development of the W. Welch
Medical Library at Johns Hopkins University. 1929.
Williams & Wilkins, Baltimore.
2743. Fleming, D. 1954. William H. Welch and the rise of
modern medicine. Little, Brown & Co., Boston. A not
too critical biography.
2744. Flexner, S. 1920. Science, 52, 417–433. An introduction
to the collected papers compiled in his honor on the oc-
casion of his 70th birthday. 3 vols. Johns Hopkins
Press, Baltimore.
2745. Flexner, S., and Flexner, J. T. 1941. William Henry Welch
and the heroic age of American medicine. Viking Press,
Inc., New York. 539 pp. (Ins. Dt. übertr. v. Tobias, L.
Thieme, Stuttgart. 1948.) This is one of the most interesting biographies written. A top-rate publication.
2746. Welch, W. H. 1920. Papers and addresses by William
Henry Welch. The Johns Hopkins Press, Baltimore.
2747. Welch, W. H. 1930. William Henry Welch at eighty. A
memorial record of celebrations around the world in his
honor. Published for the committee on the celebration

of the eightieth birthday of Doctor William Henry Welch
by the Milbank Memorial Fund, New York. 230 pp. Port.
2748. **Welch, W. H.** 1941. Medical Classics, 5, 823–939. Biography, bibliography, list of biographies. Two papers.
2749. **Welch, W. H.** (1850–1934). 1950. Bull. Hist. Med., 24,
No. 4. A large part of this publication is dedicated to
the memory of William H. Welch. Articles by Owsei,
Temkin, Cohen, Shryock, and Salomonsen.

145

WHERRY, WILLIAM P.

American bacteriologist. Noted for a number of contributions, including his discovery of tularemia, detection
of sylvatic plague, culture media, etc.

2759. **Fischer, M. H.** 1938. William P. Wherry, bacteriologist. C.
C Thomas, Publishers, Springfield, Ill. 293 pp. Port.
See review by Kofoid, C. A. 1940. Isis, 32, 165–166.
Bibliography of 82 titles.

146

WINOGRADSKY, SERGEI NIKOLAJEWITSCH

Russian bacteriologist, 1856–1953. One of the top four
great founders in bacteriology. Famous soil microbiologist.

2769. **Stainer, R. Y.** 1951. The life-work of a founder of bacteriology (Winogradsky). The Quart. Rev. Bio., 26,
35–37.
2770. **Waksman, S. A.** 1953. Sergei N. Winogradsky, his life and
work; the story of a great bacteriologist. Rutgers Univ.
Press. 150 pp. List of publications of Winogradsky,

pp. 147-150. Brief biography, selected correspondence, and a bibliography. Numerous portraits. This little book should be a building stone for a future, more comprehensive biography.

147

WRIGHT, ALMROTH EDWARD

British bacteriologist, 1861–   . A pioneer in typhoid inoculation and numerous other contributions.

2780. Colebrook, L. 1952. Bibliography of the published writings of Sir Almroth E. Wright. Heineman, Toronto.

148

YERSIN, ALEXANDRE   (ÉMILE-JOHN)

French bacteriologist, 1863–1943. Discovered the *Bacillus pestis*. Carried out classical work with Roux on diphtheria.

2790. Bernard, N., Handuroy, P., and Olivier, E. 1944. Yersin et la peste. Masson et Cie, Paris.
2791. Yersin, A. (1863–1943). 1944. Yersin et la peste. Ouvrage publié pour le cinquantenaire de la découverte du microbe de la peste. Sciences et médecine, série médicale, Rouge, Lausanne. Book published to celebrate the half-century anniversary of Yersin's discovery. It includes Yersin's own papers on the subject, a biography by Noël Bernard, and an account of the discovery by Paul Hauduroy.

149

ZINSSER, HANS

American bacteriologist and immunologist, 1878–1940. Made numerous important contributions. Noted for his work on typhus. Outstanding teacher.

2801. **Zinsser, H.** 1940. As I remember him (An autobiography). Little, Brown, & Co., Boston. An excellent and interesting autobiography.

2802. _____. 1935. Rats, lice and history. Atlantic Monthly Press, Boston. This is one of the popular classics and interesting histories concerning typhus fever.

INDEX

Abraham, E. P., 935*
Abstracts
  bacteriology, 146–172
  biological, 149, 438
  British, 7
  chemical, 151
  dairy, 1056
  dairy science, 153, 211
  general, 2–31
  immunology, 438–446
  medical, 76–81
  milk, 1055
  nutrition, 164
  papers, 148, 614
  prevention of deterioration, 165–
    166
  science, 26
  Soviet medicine, 635
Accidental scientific discoveries,
  2007
Acid-fast method, 2005
ACS (antireticular cytotoxic
  serum), 1225
Acta Microbiologica, 475
Acta Microbiologica Polonica; ...,
  182, 272
Acta Pathologica et Microbiologica
  Scandinavica, 183, 476, 477,
  615
Acta Physiologica Academiae Scientiarum Hungaricae, 184,
  478, 616
Acta Serologica et Immunologica,
  447
Acta Virologica, 479
Actinomyces, pathogenic anaer-
  obes, 753
Actinomycetales, 1457
Actinomycetes, 706–707, 1459
  guide to classification and iden-
    tification, 707, 913
  of the mouth, 1071

Adams, C. W., 1994
Adaptation, microorganisms, 1087
Advances
  medical, 91–92
  virus research, 185
Agar-agar, 1010, 1971
Age
  and achievement, 1995
  of bacteriologists for best work,
    1994–1996
Ageing, bacteria, 1210
Agents of disease and host re-
  sistance, 412
Agglutination
  bacteria, 2005
  red blood cells, 2005
Ainsworth, G. C., 382
Air, 717–721, 2695–2701
  sterilization, use of glycol, 2005
Air-borne infection, 1892
Alcohol
  beverages, 1766
  fermentation, 1264
Alexander, 1594
Alexander, J., 1417
Allen, E. K., 1689
Allen, O. N., 1689
Allen, P. W., 1957
Allen, R. M., 1353
Allergy, 1224, 1239, 1333
  symposium, history of, 1246
Almquist, E., 1958
America
  colonial, epidemics, 1113
  Latin, scientific papers, 30
American
  bacteriologists, society, 659–
    667
  history of epidemiology, 1118
  men of science, 1936
  microscope builders, 1382

*References are to entry numbers, unless otherwise noted.

181

Conn, H. W., 662
Cook, M. T., 1824
Cooperation, primitive organisms, 1087
Cosslett, V. E., 1399, 1407, 1414
Costantin, J., 2472
Court, T. H., 1360
Cowan, S. T., 260
Cox, G. J., 1072
Crane, E. J., 9, 41, 91, 126, 600
Crawhall, T. C., 1771
Creasey, C. H., 2696
Cressoc, M., 2584
Crowngall, etiology of, 1562
Cultivation of bacteria, 1008–1038
Culture, nonsulphur purple and brown bacteria, 809
Culture media, 1017, 2759
Cultivation
  animal and plant cells, 1873
  viruses and rickettsiae, 1038
Cummins, S. L., 2303
Cumulative book index, 328
Current list of medical literature, 80
Currie, M., 2008
Currie, P., 2008
"Cyclogenic" theory, 1179
Cytology, bacteria, 1444–1466

Dairy
  bacteriology, 1048–1056, 2594
  microbiology, 1050
  science abstracts, 153, 211, 1056
Dakin, H. D., 849
Dale, 2005
Damon, S. R., 1142
Danish scientists, 1979
Darmbrand-Enteritis necroticans, 755
Davies, R., 1087
Davis, G. E., 1708
Davis, J. B., 1504
Davison, W. C., 1101
Dawes, B., 1769
Dawson, P. M., 2615
DDT, 872

Death, bacteria, 1207–1211
de Kruif, P., 1974, 1975
DeLamater, 1466
Delaporte, B., 1465
Delaunay, A., 2477
Delbrück, M., 1263
"Delft School," 1980
Den Dooren De Jong, L. E., 2037
Dental, 1066–1075
Dental bacteriology, 1066
Dental caries, 1072
Descour, L., 2478
Desderi, P., 733
Design and chance in discovery and invention, 2009
Deterioration, materials, 1267
Deterioration, prevention of, abstracts, 165–166
Deutsche Gestalten, 1970
Deutsche Nationalbibliographie, 329
Devaine, 987
Devonshire, R. L., 2511
Dewberry, E. B., 1142, 1967
Dibdin, 1912
Dictionaries, 382–388
  antibiosis, 387, 903
  bacteriological equivalents; ..., 388
  bibliography of interlingual ..., 383
  communicable diseases, polyglot, 384
  fungi, 382
  microbiology, 386
  pathogenes, 385
Dienes, L., 997
Dimier, L., 2080
Dingle, J. H., 789
Diphtheria, 2790–2791
Directory
  biological laboratories, 548
  commercial and college laboratories and personnel in North America, 549
  international scientific organizations, 679
  medical and biological research institutes of the U.S.S.R., 555

Parker, R. A., 2614
Partridge, W., 388
Pascher, A., 808
Pasteur, L., 692, 719, 721, 733,
    848, 963, 1052, 1221, 1222,
    1231, 1260, 1726, 1820, 1821,
    1974, 1978, 1982, 1983, 1958,
    1964, 2005, 2008, 2470–2515,
    2695
Pasteur, Madame, 2512
Pasteur's son-in-law, 2501
Patent information, sources, 126
Pathogenic anaerobic organisms of
    the Actinomyces group, 753
Pathology, 1488–1493
  cell, 1230
  insect, 1291, 1293
Patterson, A. M., 9, 41, 91, 126,
    600
Pauley, A., 79, 1115
Pavlovskii, E. N., 2391
Peace or pestilence, 1890
Pearse, L., 1661
Pedersen, K. O., 1779
Peel, J. L., 808
Pelczar, M. J., 1014
Pellegrini, F., 2232, 2233
Penicillin, 929, 931, 941, 943,
    950, 957, 962, 2005, 2007;
    see also Chain, E. B.; Flem-
    ing, A.; Florey, H. W.
  abstracts, 914
  bibliography, 896, 899
  chemistry of, 967
  prelude to discovery, 946
  story of, 959, 963
Periodicals
  animal experimentation, 793–798
  catalog, 596
  history of medicine, 1333
  medical, 599, 603
  Russian literature, 639
  sources for, 596–604
  World list of, 598
Perkins, J. J., 1541
Perkins, R. G., 994
Perspectives and horizons in
    microbiology, 835
Peste, 2791
Petri, 719, 721

Petrie, G. F., 2392
Petroleum, bacteriology, 1503–
    1504
Pettenkofer, M., 1970, 2525–2531
Pflanzenschutzliteratur, Bibli-
    ographie, 1554
Pharmazeutische Zentralhalle für
    Deutchland, 295
Pharmazie; ..., 296
Phase microscope, 1428–1434
Phillips, C. J., 1777
Phillips, M. D., 1596
Photographs, presidents of the
    Society of American Bacteri-
    ologists, 661
Physical agents, harmful effect on
    bacteria, 1536–1544
Physical techniques in biological
    research, 1414
Physicians desk reference to
    pharmaceutical specialties,
    552
Physiology
  bacterial, 1100, 1208, 1514–
    1527, 1536, 1542
  and biochemistry of bacteria,
    409, 885
Pijper, A., 1463
Pinkerton, H., 1613
Pillemer, L., 1794
Piper, D. L., 964
Pirie, N. W., 1455
Pirquet, C. F., 1239
Plague, sylvatic, 2759; see also
    Kitasato, S.; Yersin, A.
Plant
  cells, cultivation of, 1873
  diseases, 584, 1449, 1554–1566,
    1751
  pathogens, manual, 992
  pathology, 2634–2635
  viruses, 1819–1835
Plasma substitutes, bibliography,
    1249
Plenk, H. 1403
Pleomorphism, bacteriology, 1184
Pochon, J., 1685
Podach, E. F., 2317, 2619
Polish literature, anaerobic bac-
    teria, 745

INDEX